NATURE AND GOD

PUBLISHER'S NOTE

Adventures in Faith is a series of books for
people with inquiring minds. These writings
represent the viewpoints of authors from dif-
fering traditions and various parts of the world.
Some may offer frankly unorthodox interpreta-
tions of the Christian faith, while others may
apply or adapt to new situations classic positions of the Church. These books may either
complement or contradict one another, but
they share a common purpose to say something
pertinent at the frontiers where the Church
meets the world today and where faith reaches
out to meet the needs of the future.

NATURE
AND
GOD

120

L. Charles Birch

THE WESTMINSTER PRESS
Philadelphia

LIBRARY OF CONGRESS CATALOG CARD No. 66–10066

To
CHARLES HARTSHORNE

Published by The Westminster Press ®
Philadelphia, Pennsylvania

PRINTED IN THE UNITED STATES OF AMERICA

CONTENTS

PREFACE

THE concept of God's operations in the universe as a series of fitful interventions from a supernatural sphere overlaying the natural is quite unacceptable to science. No reconciliation is possible between religious fundamentalism and modern science. On the other hand, the traditional thinking of science, sometimes called mechanism, is quite unreconcilable with any reasoned Christian position. Far from there being any truce or understanding between science and religion, it is nearer the truth to say that the supernaturalist tradition in theology and traditional science are being driven further and further apart. Many scientists see the issues this way. Some of them, for example Wren-Lewis,[1] see the possible consequences as disastrous.

And yet there is hope. Within science and within theology and philosophy, some radical changes are taking place that are altering the whole traditional position. These changes are opening up a new and constructive way of looking at the natural world, in the light both of science and of Christian insights. These changes are little known where they ought to be known. Because of them this generation could be within closer reach of an understanding of nature and God than any previous generation.

A religion that seeks to insulate itself from the wisdom of the world is likely to lose its life in the modern world. 'The history of religion', says Professor John E. Smith, 'is filled with examples of causes lost because their proponents believed it possible to preserve their ancient wisdom free from all the contaminating contact with insights derived from general experience and secular knowledge. A rational religion cannot afford to make that mistake.'[2]

The dominant mood of the twentieth century is specialization. Attempts to discover any unity in knowledge or any overall synthesis of religion and culture are frowned upon. There have been periods in history marked by the great attempts at a synthesis. The Christian scholars of the Alexandrian school in the third century under Clement and Origen excluded no part of learning or religion in their attempts to make sense of the world they lived in. Another great period of synthesis was the eighteenth century in Cambridge, when a professor of medicine, Ralph Cudworth, could also be a professor of theology. He belonged to that group of synthesists who became known as the Cambridge Platonists.

Then again, no one can read the works of the giants in British science in the century or so preceding Charles Darwin without realizing that the whole of religion and learning was their field. They were not afraid to try to relate their special studies to the meaning of the whole. Scientists were amateurs then. The result was that their scientific writings were done within the context of issues that could concern all thinking people. When John Ray, Robert Chambers and Robert Brown wrote about biology, they wrote so that anyone who wished to make the effort could understand. The same was true of John Dalton, Humphry Davy and Michael Faraday in physics.[3] The same was true of Charles Darwin and his protagonist, T. H. Huxley. They wrote with a simplicity and directness that made what they had to say relevant to all who wished to read.

Charles Darwin was well aware that what he wrote about could have a profound effect on man's understanding of his total environment as well as of himself. In the final chapter of *The Origin of Species*, he predicted a revolution in a dozen or more fields of biology as a result of his findings, and as well in the new fields of psychology and anthropology. Before the final edition was published, it was clear that the importance of the book for religion was equally profound. T. H. Huxley wrote about all these fields. He called his addresses sermons. He believed they could do what the sermon was meant to do in the Church. He was telling everyman of the relevance of the new learning to him. His zeal was evangelical. It was relevant. It got across.

This century has its synthesists. They do not as yet claim any general attention in an age of specialization and analysis in science, philosophy and religion. However, I believe their time is approaching. Notable among them have been the process philosophers A. N. Whitehead, Charles Hartshorne and Paul Tillich. They have influenced my thoughts more than I can tell. They, and others like them, have given me the urge to think in fields that I can never know in equal depth. It has meant that I have had to write about history, philosophy and theology as well as science. This involves a risk. Mistakes there will surely be. But if the frontiers of understanding and meaning are pushed a little further forward for some of my readers, then it has been worth while.

This book is an expanded version of the 1964 Centenary Livingstone Lectures of Camden Congregational Theological College, Sydney. The foundation of these lectures provides for a treatment of some subject dealing with relationships between science and religion. The lectures were given in the University of Sydney to an audience consisting of students of all faculties and members of the general public. I have written for a similar group and from the point of view of a biologist who is also a Christian, though one who may not measure up to the judgment of some who regard themselves as the trustees of orthodoxy. I have not written primarily about my own special field of biology, though biology has a central place in the argument. This book is really about God. It is anything but traditional in its approach. Indeed, the traditional approach seems to have struck a brick wall in the mind of many a modern man. It is because I find a real point of contact with the modern questioning student mind in what I have put down, that I am hopeful it may help others.

My scientific colleagues might well say, 'Cobbler, stick to your last'. But we have been doing that in science for long enough. I have attempted what is not a very popular endeavour in our generation. It is to cover a canvas so broad that the whole cannot possibly be the specialized knowledge of any single person. The attempt may be presumptuous. I have made it because of the urgency that we try, in spite of the vastness of the subject.

I would not have written had I not discovered something for myself that makes sense of the world of specialized knowledge in which I live. The most critical time in my own search for understanding was as a young research student, dissatisfied with the answers of what called itself orthodox Christianity and excited about science. I am eternally grateful that I was introduced at so critical a time to a realm of experience and thought in liberal Christian thinking and process philosophy that I had not known before. To Kenneth Newman of the Student Christian Movement in the University of Adelaide I owe my initiation to that new world of thought.

This book is dedicated to Professor Charles Hartshorne, now of the University of Texas, whom I regard as the greatest student of A. N. Whitehead. I have reason for thinking that Whitehead agreed with this judgment. He introduced me to the sensitive side of nature that science tends to ignore. He helped me to see all the world in a different light. Much of my understanding of evolutionary biology and my interest in the philosophical problems of evolution springs from a lasting friendship with Professor Theodosius Dobzhansky of the Rockefeller Institute, New York. To the Warden of Camden Congregational Theological College in Sydney, the Reverend John Garrett, I owe more than I can say. He was initially responsible for getting me to put my thoughts together. He saw the process through to a final manuscript. His constant help has prevented me from making more errors than might otherwise have occurred. None of these colleagues will agree with all I have said, nor can they be held responsible for anything that I have said! But I could not have got on without them. Finally, I want to thank Miss Barbara Brett who has been meticulous in typing the manuscript and has greatly helped in editing as she worked through it.

L. C. B.

Sydney, July **1964**

1

THE UNIVERSE:
A MACHINE OR A BIRTH?

The whole created universe groans in all its parts as if in the pangs of childbirth.   Romans 8. 22 (NEB).

Becoming is no longer the enemy of permanence but its ever- lasting foundation.   Charles Hartshorne.[1]

The God of the Australians

IN the year 1676 a book was published entitled *Terre Australe Connue*. In it the author Foigny described an ideal island in the southern seas. This was one of many utopias imagined by writers in the seventeenth and eighteenth centuries. All was sweetness and light, in contrast to the wars, inequalities and other hardships at home in Europe. The inhabitants of *Terre Australe*, whom Foigny called Australians, were descended, not from Adam, but from a being who had never fallen. Furthermore, the Australians were deists; that is, they believed that God had made a world perfect and complete for man to languish in. There was no more to do, either for God or man, save to enjoy the perfect bliss of *Terre Australe* for ever.[2]

It is a paradox of history that it was in part their interpretation of science which led men like Foigny to such a concept of nature and God. His was perhaps an extreme version of a view that was widely held in the sixteenth, seventeenth and eighteenth centuries, the first three centuries of modern science. This might appear to be a contradiction, for after all utopia literally means 'no place' in reality. But for these dreamers of utopia it was the paradise God had made complete and perfect once and for all but which Adam had lost. Their science and their religion combined to make a natural theology in which all was sweetness and light with no place for imperfection and tragedy. If this did not quite fit the picture at home, then maybe it did beyond the horizon. With a little bit of imagination, you could make out the real paradise on earth which was God's creation.

We tend to think of the rebirth of science in the sixteenth century as being the birth of a conflict with religion, but before the century was out this same science was being largely used as a mainstay for belief in what became known as deism. This is the theory of the completed mechanical universe presided over by a divine mechanic. As Basil Willey has remarked, 'Whether one contemplated the infinitely great by the optic glass of the Tuscan artist, or the infinitely little through the microscope of Malpighi, one received at every turn a new assurance that all was according to the Ordainer of order and mystical mathematics of the city of heaven.'[2] Science was unveiling a universe that looked like a vast machine. What had God to do with the machinery? The answer the deists gave was—very little now, but he made it all in the first place. God was the cosmic mechanic, the maker of the machine. How did they come to think of the universe in such terms?

The Universe as Mechanism

Copernicus had given the world a picture of the universe in mechanical and mathematical terms. Galileo added to this picture and put the emphasis for science on measuring. Indeed, he said that only that which is measurable is real. These measurable qualities he called primary qualities; shape, size, position, and mass which was added later. These are the properties of bodies studied in mechanics. Bodies appear to have other qualities to be sure, such as colour, sound, smell, taste and so on. These he called secondary qualities. They were, he said, entirely due to the people perceiving them. A feather brushed on the skin tickles, but you do not say that tickling is a property of the feather. Nor should you suppose that secondary qualities are real properties of things. Galileo's world had exactly the same set of limited properties as the ancient Greek world of atomism of Democritus, Epicurus and Lucretius. Their world consisted of atoms of matter moving in empty space. The atoms had only those same qualities that Galileo called primary qualities. The same point of view is pushed further by Newton who, in one fell swoop, provided one universal principle of gravitation to account for the movement of all bodies great or small. The stars in their courses and the apple that falls from the tree both move according to the same rules.

Hesse[3] points out that the success of Newton's system in explaining the motion of bodies led to the demand of the seventeenth century that all explanation in science should be in terms of mass particles or atoms moving in space. This is the 'billiard ball' universe of which Whitehead said, 'The course of nature is conceived as being merely the fortunes of matter in its adventure through space'.[4] In his *Essay Concerning Human Understanding* (1690), Locke declared that he only needed to know the position and motion of the bits and pieces that constituted rhubarb and opium and he would then be able to predict that rhubarb would purge and opium would make a man sleep. It was the view expressed later by Laplace in his claim that if he were given the original positions and motions of every particle in the universe, he could predict the entire course of subsequent events. William Blake said that to teach the atomism of science was 'to educate a fool to build a universe with farthing balls'. It did not take long for the inventors of the mechanical universe to see that there was nothing for God to do in it. He was progressively dismissed from it, except in so far as he might be regarded as the one who made it in the first place. Newton did not dismiss God altogether. He was unable to account for the precise orbs of the planets in terms of his mechanics. So he supposed that God personally intervened when they went off their paths. The universe was like a self-winding clock that ran pretty well on the whole, but it could get out of time. Then it was necessary for God to return to regulate it. Newton's contemporaries could see that further discoveries in science were likely to replace even this limited role he gave to God. And such was indeed what happened.[5]

And so was revived in the seventeenth century from its Greek origin the famous mechanistic theory of nature. The physical world was to be explained entirely as the consequence of the disposition of masses which moved each other according to their mass and to the distances between them. Whitehead remarked, 'It is a view that has reigned supreme ever since'.[4]

Living Organisms as Machines

What of biology? If we were to choose a single year to mark the birth of modern biology it would be 1543. Not only was this a red-letter year for physics, being the date of publication of Copernicus' *Revolution of the Celestial Orbs*, it was also the year of publication of the first great work of modern biology, *The Fabric of the Human Body* by Vesalius. As the title implies, Vesalius considered the body to be a fabric; the workmanship of 'the great craftsman'. On the foundations of Vesalius' anatomy, the Englishman William Harvey was to initiate a revival of the science of physiology with the publication in 1628 of his *Anatomical Dissertation concerning the Motion of the Heart and Blood*. All this new information from biology fitted very nicely into the mechanistic doctrines of Locke and Hobbes. But it was for Hobbes' more brilliant contemporary Descartes to give explicit development to the mechanistic theory of nature in the living part of the world. 'Give me matter and motion and I will construct a universe,' he said, and this is precisely what he found in the works of Vesalius and Harvey. Here were levers and joints, pumps and valves with which to build a machine. And this is what Descartes did in what was the first scientific textbook of mechanistic physiology, his *Traité de l'homme* (1664). Descartes was trained as an engineer. His textbook was an engineer's conception of how the body works.

Of course there were problems when Descartes came to consider the brain and the human mind. It seemed quite plain to him that animals could be described as automata, but it was difficult to accept this as an adequate account of the human mind. So Descartes postulated two sorts of entities, matter and mind. Man was a machine but with the difference that he had a mind 'annexed' to it. Hence was born the Cartesian doctrine of the bifurcation of nature which has had a profound influence on human thought ever since. The relation of matter to mind remained a mystery in Descartes' scheme. As to God, he was outside nature. Butterfield summarizes Descartes thus:

> God, the human soul and the whole realm of spiritual things, however, escaped imprisonment in the process of mechanization, and were superadded presences, flitting vaporously amongst the cog-wheels, the pulleys, the steel castings of a relentless world-machine. It was very difficult to show how these two planes of existence could ever have come to intersect, or at what point mind or soul could ever join up with matter.[6]

Descartes had a profound influence on thought about nature.[7] Some claim that he has influenced the background thinking of scientists more than any other philosopher. He had a direct influence in the first mechanistic movement in biochemistry headed by Franciscus Sylvius of Leyden, in the discovery of the muscular nature of the heart by Nicholas Steno, and in the application of methods of physics to biology by Giovanni Borelli, Sanctorius and others.[8] Des-

cartes gave a philosophical status to the mechanical pro-
cedures of science which were to prove so successful in
analysing the world. All this was commendable. Mechanism
has had its triumphs; it is possible that science would have
advanced more slowly without the mechanistic formulation
of Descartes. But the subsequent part of the story is different. When carried to an extreme, the mechanistic doctrine
of Descartes was to have disastrous consequences in man's
view of the universe.

In Descartes' scheme God seemed to be outside the
system except in so far as 'God breathed a living soul' into
man. A doctrine of God in the living world was developed
much more explicitly in England, notably by John Ray,
the Cambridge botanist. His book *The Wisdom of God
Manifested in the Works of the Creation* (first published
late in the seventeenth century, then expanded and reprinted many times in later centuries) determined, more
than any other, the character of interpretation of nature
until Darwin's time.[9] 'I mean by the works of creation,' he
wrote, 'the works created by God at first, and by him con-
served to this day in the same state and condition in which
they were first made.'[10] The study of nature revealed the
'wisdom of God in his original design'. Ray was not the
first biologist to argue in this way. Indeed, the greatest
experimental biologist of antiquity, the physician Galen
(AD 150-200) was led by his studies of anatomy to a view
that all the parts of the body were designedly fixed by a
wise and far-seeing God.[11] For Ray, the adaptive camou-
flage of the tiger, the perfection of the human eye for seeing,
the maintenance of the right ratio between the sexes, all
argued for the perfection of both the blueprint of nature
drawn by the great architect and the act of creation itself.
Moreover, the long recital of adaptations of plants and
animals in itself 'proved infallibly' the existence of God as
he forcibly tells his reader in the concluding paragraphs of
his book. Ray wrote about organ after organ of the human

body, the parental solicitude of birds and the non-appearance of wasps until the plums are ripe and other adaptations as evidence of God's designing hand. Even the most vile insect, he says, provides us with medicine. And as for plagues of insects, they are sent by God to chastise us. God, having made nature, had left it except for such interventions. These were the only present 'acts of God'. You could say it was a lawyer's view of the nature of God's activity. Ray recognizes what he calls 'errors and bungles' in nature. These he attributes to a 'plastic nature' or 'vegetative soul' of the living organism, a concept he borrowed from Cudworth. But all the wonders of design in nature are to be attributed to the wisdom of the original creation which somehow overrules 'plastic nature' in these instances.[9, 12]

There can be no serious doubt that Ray's book contributed to the general atmosphere of satisfied optimism in the eighteenth century which Willey has descriptively called cosmic Toryism'.[2] This state of thought was summed up in Pope's famous six lines set forth in the *Essay on Man*:

> *All nature is but art, unknown to thee;*
> *All chance direction which thou canst not see;*
> *All discord, harmony not understood;*
> *All partial evil, universal good;*
> *And spite of pride, in erring reason's spite*
> *One truth is clear: whatever is is right.*

This was the best of all possible worlds. The latter phrase which Voltaire puts into the mouth of Pangloss in *Candide* came from Leibnitz. But Liebnitz did not imply, as others have, contentment with the whole cosmic scheme. He offered a variety of solutions to the problem of evil and tended to conclude that even with evil as an ingredient, this world is better than any conceivable alternative. Voltaire ridiculed the proposition in *Candide* by asking, 'If this is the best of all possible worlds, then what are the others like?'

The historical importance of Ray in this story is surely that he, more than any other biologist in the seventeenth and eighteenth centuries, provided the details of a deistic view of nature. His book was persuasive for his contemporaries, though rather boring for us. Linnaeus, the prince of botanists of the eighteenth century, who was born two years after Ray's death, accepted his argument. In his own essay *On the Increase of the Habitable Earth* (1743), Linnaeus wrote:

> Scripture and reason equally assures us that this astounding machine, the universe, was produced and created by an infinite Architect. . . . He who has ordered all things with the most singular wisdom, and has regulated the number of the offspring of every kind of animal with a proportion so exact, employed certainly as accurate a calculation in creating them.[13]

Biology of the seventeenth century headed by Ray reinforced the natural theology that had been constructed by physics and astronomy in the sixteenth century. For three centuries, until the middle of the nineteenth century, nature was regarded as a sure basis for belief in God, indeed a surer basis than theology. 'Evidences' for religion meant nature not theology. After all, theology had been a constant source of dispute since the Reformation. This had led to hatred, persecution, even war. Nature was the great alternative to the confused religious background of the seventeenth, eighteenth and early nineteenth centuries.

From the uncertainty of traditional theology, the deists of the eighteenth century invented their own 'natural' theology. A list of their names is a list of largely forgotten men; scarcely any one of the theologians amongst them was of any distinction. But they left their mark. The one name that stands for them all is William Paley whose *Natural Theology* (1802) was to become their Bible.

The source of their inspiration was twofold—nature and the Stoics. They turned back the pages, not of the Bible, but of Greek history. In the Stoic view of the universality of natural law, they found the basis of their world view. Whereas the Stoics used this as a point of departure for belief in a universal community of men, the Christian deists found in it their basis for belief in God. The classic formulation of Stoic laws is found in the writings of Cicero, and to him the deists turned for their arguments. 'The divine mind', declared Cicero in *The Laws*, 'is the supreme law.' From Cicero's *On the Nature of the Gods* they resurrected the analogy of the watch and the watchmaker for the universe and its creator. The analogy became the central 'argument' of Paley's *Natural Theology* and of a whole collection of similar books with revealing titles such as *Physicotheology*, *Water Theology* and even *Insect Theology*.[14]

Paley's *Natural Theology* became the standard textbook of the educated Englishman. Something of its status may be gained from the fact that it remained an alternative to logic in the entrance examination for Cambridge until 1920. Charles Darwin knew it so well that he says in a letter to Sir John Lubbock in 1859, 'I could almost formerly have said it by heart'. This remark is preceded by the very surprising comment, 'I do not think I hardly ever admired a book more than Paley's *Natural Theology*'.[15] One hardly can tell what it was that Darwin so admired. Perhaps it was the catalogue of adaptations rather than the deistic conclusions.

If Paley were the theologian of deism, then Locke was its unwitting philosopher. Probably no philosophical writings gave more reinforcement to deism than Locke's two works *An Essay concerning Human Understanding* (1690) and *The Reasonableness of Christianity* (1695). 'The works of nature', said Locke, 'in every part of them sufficiently evidence a Deity.' God is to be known from the 'evidence' of nature which provides the basis of a rational proof of God's existence. The proof was given by Locke. How different this was from the Cambridge Platonists, some of whom were Locke's contemporaries! They looked to 'inner experience' as the root of religion. This emphasis was an oasis of spiritual perception and human sympathy in an age in which the dominant mood was for proving God as the end of an argument. This was the mood which persisted with Locke's philosophical backing until the zenith of deism in the first half of the eighteenth century. Locke, unlike the deists who found support in his arguments, left the door open for 'revelation' in religion. That 'Jesus is the Messiah' was the one revelation needed for the Christian in Locke's scheme. This was one bit of information that came by channels other than reason.

Protests against Mechanism

The tide had to turn. Even as early as the opening of the eighteenth century, the great argument from nature for the existence of the divine mechanic was becoming less sure. Dissentient voices came from four sources: theology, philosophy, the poets and biology.

The first voice of theology was hardly influential in its own time. It came from the little band of Cambridge Platonists in the seventeenth century. In 1678 Ralph Cudworth published *The Intellectual System of the Universe*. This book, like other works of this devoted group of Cambridge theologians, was written in protest against the materialism of Hobbes. It was written in the light of the new science, but was out of sympathy with its most famous interpreter, Descartes. It rejected the mechanical framework of deism and the glib formulation of the traditional dogmas for a feeling for the 'spirit' of Christian faith that transformed lives. So Cudworth wrote, 'The root of all atheism consists in making senseless matter the only self-existent thing, and the original of all things . . . and mind as nothing but local motion in the organic parts of a man's body'.[16] He affirms the reality of mind as the ground of all that is. For our present purposes, Cudworth's book has a second great interest. It was an *exposé* of evil in a world that was supposed to be created once and for all perfect by an all-powerful being. Everything in the garden was not rosy; it was *not* the best of all possible worlds. But how could the deists equate these facts with the notion of a divine all-powerful engineer? Cudworth raised the issue clearly enough. But he was unable to find a way out of the dilemma. As Hume showed later, no answer was possible within the framework of deism. Here is Cudworth's dilemma.

> Consider for a moment the problem of evil. There are four possibilities with regard to evil. Either God is able but not willing to overcome it, or perchance he is not able though he may be willing. It may be that he is neither able nor willing to overcome evil. Or it remains that he is both able and willing. Only the last would seem to be worthy of a good God, and it does not happen.

There is no answer to that dilemma if we think that God is the omnicompetent engineer. Are we to suppose that 'God himself doth all immediately and as it were with his own hands form the body of every gnat and fly'? This was the question Cudworth put. He gave no answer. Darwin was to take it up later on.

A much more direct attack on deism came from the theologian William Law. His *Case of Reason* (1732) was an answer to Matthew Tindal's *Christianity as Old as Creation*. Law anticipates Bishop Butler's argument against deism in *The Analogy* and attacks the shallowness of Tindal's deism, claiming that it reduced God to the measure of human capacity. Law is now chiefly remembered for his other writings; he had a deep and lasting influence on John Wesley and other leaders of the Evangelical revival.

The decisive criticism of deism came from the philosophers Berkeley, Butler and Hume. Berkeley set out his new view of the universe in his *Principles of Natural Knowledge* (1710), *Three Dialogues* (1713) and *Alciphron* (1732). Locke had argued for a universe consisting entirely of mechanical bodies that interacted with one another. The impact of bodies on our nervous system gave rise to 'ideas' in the mind about these bodies. What we are directly aware of are the 'ideas'. Berkeley argued that if ideas are the only objects of direct awareness, then there is no warrant for belief in 'matter' as something independent of our ideas. Everyday things which we perceive are really collections of 'ideas'. But ideas can only exist in a mind. The universal mind that held all these ideas was the mind of God. The deists on the other hand glorify matter, and end up with a picture little better than atheism. Bishop Butler's *The Analogy of Religion, Natural and Revealed, to the Constitution and Course of Nature* was the most formidable work that the deistic controversy called forth. The deists assumed they knew all about God. Butler points to the perplexity and ambiguity of life and exposes the slick answer of an over-confident argument. He provides no proof for the existence of God, nor did he need to. He was exposing fallacies and had no intention of providing a new philosophy of religion. What we read into nature is not clear but full of ambiguity. Nor should we be surprised that the insights of Christian faith are also marked with a certain obscurity. This is the *analogy*, since neither religion nor nature leads to an irrefutable proof of God's existence. So his denial of deism is not a denial of religion but a guide to a more genuine faith.

Hume attacks just about all the traditional certainties. In his works we find the most critical analysis of both the presuppositions of science and the certainties of the deists. *An Enquiry concerning Human Understanding* (1748) provides a criticism of the inductive method of science that has never been answered. The *Dialogues concerning Natural Religion* (1779) are a devastating repudiation of the argument for God from design in nature. The God you will find for a mechanical universe, Hume says, will be the sort of God who makes the mechanism. The argument for deism is the argument for a mechanic, but this is not the God of Christianity. He is left with a feeling for purpose in the universe and some role for God, though the precise role is difficult to see. In *A Treatise of Human Nature*, Book 3 'On Morals', he raises the same question as Cudworth about evil and the omnipotence of God. If God is omnipotent, he is responsible for all the evil in the world, and if God is responsible for evil, then he is not morally good. Therefore, either there is no evil, or God is not omnipotent, or he is not morally perfect. If you maintain these three then the dilemma is inescapable. By exposing the problem, he exposes the shallowness of deism, but he declines to suggest a solution to the dilemma.[17]

The nature poets of the eighteenth and nineteenth centuries also played a part in the rejection of the mechanistic philosophy. The mechanistic universe of science was to Wordsworth 'a universe of death':

> *Sweet is the lore which Nature brings;*
> *Our meddling intellect*
> *Mis-shapes the beauteous forms of things—*
> *We murder to dissect.*[18]

In the scientific analysis something had been left out. What had been left out contained all that was important. What was left behind was the skeleton of a machine which natural theology had accepted as reality. This was a murderous abstraction from reality. 'I think we are not wholly brain, magnetic mockeries . . .', wrote Tennyson.[19] William Blake called the deists 'the enemies of the human race and of universal nature.'[20] He sees 'a world in a grain of sand' and curses mechanical rationalism:

> *Mock on, Mock on, Voltaire, Rousseau:*
> *Mock on, Mock on: 'tis all in vain!*
> *You throw the sand against the wind,*
> *And the wind blows it back again.*

In their hands the universe becomes a 'mill with complicated wheels':

Reason, or the ratio of all we have already known, is not
the same that it shall be when we know more. . . .
He who sees the Infinite in all things, sees God.
He who sees the Ratio only, sees himself only.[21]

Bronowski comments, 'Reasoning, the mill, and the machine worlds of Newton and of Locke are already (in this poem) parts of one symbol about 1788 when Blake etched . . . these sentences'.[22]

The 'romantic' reaction of the poets brought into sharp focus the discord between the aesthetic intuitions of mankind and the mechanism of science. 'Thus we gain from these poets', says Whitehead, 'the doctrine that a philosophy of nature must concern itself at least with these six notions: chance, value, eternal objects, endurance, organism, interfusion.'[4] They were concepts which for centuries had hardly belonged to literature.

No poem illustrates more completely how the poets found themselves out of step with orthodox deism and mechanistic science than Tennyson's *In Memoriam*, published in 1850.[23] Begun as a lament over a personal bereavement, it continued as a lament for the passing of spiritual values in the harsh dawn of a new age. The whole spectrum of nature that was revealed by Lyell's *Principles of Geology* and Chambers' *Vestiges of the Natural History of Creation* seemed to Tennyson quite opposed to the concepts of the deists. The picture of nature was becoming less and less like the garden paradise of the deists and of natural theology. So Tennyson wrote:

Are God and Nature then at strife,
That Nature lends such evil dreams?
So careful of the type she seems,
So careless of the single life;

That I, considering everywhere
Her secret meaning in her deeds,
And finding that of fifty seeds
She often brings but one to bear,

I falter where I firmly trod.
And falling with my weight of cares
Upon the great world's altar-stairs
That slope thro' darkness up to God

I stretch lame hands of faith, and grope,
And gather dust and chaff, and call
To what I feel is Lord of all,
And faintly trust the larger hope. . . .

Man her last work, who seem'd so fair,
Such splendid purpose in his eyes,
Who roll'd the psalm to wintry skies,
Who built him fanes of fruitless prayer,

Who trusted God and love indeed
And love Creation's final law—
Tho' Nature, red in tooth and claw
With ravine, shriek'd against his creed. . . .

And in the face of all this he cries:

What hope of answer, or redress?
Behind the veil, behind the veil.

To someone who told him that all his doubts about traditional faith were of the devil he replies:

There lives more faith in honest doubt,
Believe me, than in half the creeds.

The hope Tennyson eventually finds is that man, recognizing himself as a product of nature, will consciously become involved in nature's struggle and

Move upward, working out the beast,
And let the ape and tiger die. . . .

No longer half akin to brute,
For all we thought and loved and did,
And hoped, and suffer'd, is but seed
Of what in them is flower and fruit. . . .

That God, which ever lives and loves,
One God, one law, one element,
And one far-off divine event,
To which the whole creation moves.

And so nine years before Charles Darwin had published *The Origin of Species*, Tennyson had rejected the concept of creation as complete and perfect. He wrote the epitaph of three centuries.

By the latter part of the eighteenth century biology itself brought rumblings of an approaching storm. The idea of nature as a centre of change and transformation, rather than of static perfection, was being suggested by a number of biologists and geologists throughout the latter part of the eighteenth century and right up to Charles Darwin's time. These were the disturbers of Tennyson's equanimity. Erasmus Darwin, grandfather of Charles, was one of them. His evolutionary ideas were set out in his long poem *Zoonomia* (1794). The great French biologist Buffon is probably the first to suggest the idea of an evolutionary branching tree of organisms. He was in a good position to generalize on the living world, having published *Histoire Naturelle* in forty-four volumes between 1749 and 1804! The branching tree of life was eventually to replace the *Scala Natura* or straight ladder of nature in which each rung of the ladder stood for a species or group of species separated from each other by unbridgeable gaps. By 1816 the Frenchman Lamarck had published his theory of evolution in *Histoire Naturelle des Animaux sans Vertèbres.*

In his preface to *The Origin of Species* Darwin mentioned 34 biologists who had recognized the possibility of what we now call evolutionary transformation. (It is interesting to remember that he wrote his book scarcely ever using the word 'evolution'.) There were plenty of ideas in the air about transformation and change. There seems little doubt that it was this atmosphere that led the Earl of Bridgewater to leave a sum of money to the Royal Society for the preparation of the treatise which was to bear his name. The sole purpose of his bequest was to commission a group of distinguished scientists to bring Paley's *Natural Theology* up to date. They did just that. Their contributions showed only too clearly that the monolithic picture of nature and nature's God that had stood for three centuries was being rent from all sides. It was obvious that there was no agreement amongst these various authors as to the problem of creation.

The storm clouds had been gathering. They burst upon the world in the year 1859, with the publication of Charles Darwin's *The Origin of Species*.

The Darwinian Crisis

It is a mistake to suppose that the impact of Darwin upon religion had to do primarily with a conflict with a literal interpretation of the book of Genesis. It was more far-reaching than that. Darwin's thesis struck in three ways at the natural theology which had become the unstable foundation of so much religious belief.

First, instead of being made once and for all complete and perfect, *the living world was and always had been in process of being made*. Secondly, Darwin pointed to some of the processes of its growth, and *the natural selection of chance variations* replaced the idea of design according to a preordained blueprint. The very phrase hit at the whole concept of design. This point has never been more clearly put than by Thomas Henry Huxley in 1864. He was replying to a critic of Darwin who wanted to retain the old watch–watchmaker analogy of Paley which is referred to by Huxley as 'Teleology'. Huxley's statement gives the essence of the theory of natural selection:

> For the notion that every organism has been created as it is and launched straight at a purpose, Mr Darwin substitutes the conception of something which may fairly be termed a

method of trial and error. Organisms vary incessantly; of these variations the few meet with surrounding conditions which suit them and thrive; the many are unsuited and become extinguished.

According to Teleology, each organism is like a rifle bullet fired straight at a mark; according to Darwin, organisms are like grapeshot of which one hits something and the rest fall wide.

For the teleologist an organism exists because it was made for the conditions in which it is found; for the Darwinian an organism exists because, out of many of its kind, it is the only one which has been able to persist in the conditions in which it is found.

Teleology implies that the organs of every organism are perfect and cannot be improved; the Darwinian theory simply affirms that they work well enough to enable the organism to hold its own against such competitors as it has met with, but admits the possibility of indefinite improvement. But an example may bring into clearer light the profound opposition between the ordinary teleological and the Darwinian, conception.

Cats catch mice, small birds and the like, very well. Teleology tells us that they do so because they were expressly constructed for so doing—that they are perfect mousing apparatuses, so perfectly and so delicately adjusted that no one of their organs could be altered, without the change involving the alteration of all the rest. Darwinism affirms on the contrary, that there was no express construction concerned in the matter; but that among the multitudinous variations of the Feline stock, many of which died out from want of power to resist opposing influences, some, the cats, were better fitted to catch mice than others, whence they throve and persisted, in proportion to the advantage over their fellows thus offered to them.

Far from imagining that cats exist *in order* to catch mice well, Darwinism supposes that cats exist *because* they catch mice well—mousing being not the end, but the condition, of their existence. And if the cat-type has long persisted as we know it, the interpretation of the fact upon Darwinian principles would be, not that the cats have remained invariable, but that such varieties as have incessantly occurred have been, on the whole, less fitted to get on in the world than the existing stock.[24]

Huxley's argument is directed against Paley's concept of teleology or purposiveness in nature. It does not exclude, nor did Huxley mean to exclude, the possibility of a much wider and deeper concept of purposiveness (see Chapter 5).

The third point of Darwin's theory which hit directly at the natural theology of deism was the concept of *struggle for existence*. Tennyson had anticipated this with his phrase 'nature red in tooth and claw'. T. H. Huxley wrote of nature as 'a gigantic gladiatorial show'. How could a loving God be involved in that sort of process?

To recapitulate: creation was unfinished and continuing, it involved chance events and struggle. Natural selection took the place of the divine mechanic of natural theology. It was not a case of denying the God of natural theology; that God had now become unnecessary. It looked as though the machine made itself.

The Position Today

The story that I have tried to trace has always appeared complex and probably always will. Part of the difficulty, if we are to see any light at all, is that we must keep in mind what was happening to two interrelated concepts: the mechanistic theory of nature and the concept of God as presiding over the universe but essentially outside it (deism). Deism was the compromise which religion made with mechanism. It was really no more than a transparent frock put over the ugly skeleton of a mechanistic universe. The skeleton needed some investing with flesh and blood if any frock were to fit. This one did not. It should have been torn to shreds. Instead the garment has been preserved, at least in bits and pieces, by much of traditional religion to this day. This has happened despite the fact that informed theology has completely disposed of it. And that is the tragedy of our time. The thinking that comes out of informed theological circles today has scarcely an echo from the suburban pulpit. Suburban theology is one hundred years out of date. If you want to be informed on these matters, you have a much better chance by picking up a few paperbacks in any bookshop than by listening from the pews.

But what about the skeleton left in the cupboard, the mechanistic theory of nature? This is a more complicated problem. But again it is true to say of the average scientist, that he is still prepared to live with a concept of mechanism that is not one hundred years out of date, but three hundred years out of date. If you were to question scientists in their laboratories today you would find most of them still living with Descartes' system, though from the day it was pronounced it began to crack. Very few are at all informed by the best thinking about the nature of their calling as scientists, or the nature of the universe that modern science reveals. 'He understands what he is doing about as well as a centipede understands how he walks,' says Herbert Dingle, the historian of science; and he adds, 'He does his job well enough and he may know the immediate objective of his efforts, but how it has come about that these efforts are called for, what is their significance in relation to life as a whole, and what will be their ultimate effect, are matters on which his innocence is beyond reproach'.[25]

Most of us, be we Christians or scientists or both, are profoundly influenced by the dominant thought of the last four hundred years. We tend to cling to remnants of a discredited deism and we tend to think about nature and the universe in terms of a nineteenth-century mechanism now largely discredited. So we are confused. This is why it is important that we see what was happening to both deism and mechanism in the centuries preceding this. Cudworth, Law, Berkeley, Butler and Hume attacked both. Cudworth and Hume showed the dilemma that the evil of the world involved for deism. The poets revolted against mechanism because it left out all that was important to them. The pre-Darwin evolutionists began to show that the machine of nature, if it were a machine, was anything but a complete one, it was still being made. Darwin pushes the argument further and provides a theory of how the machine makes itself. No wonder the nineteenth century ends in utter confusion. Its God of nature was irrelevant. But that did not just leave it with a godless machine, for mechanism itself was under fire. That is the dilemma which we have inherited.[26]

A Clue from the New Testament

How, then, can there be any room for a God in a world of struggle, accident, chance, suffering and cruelty? Man seemed to be groping for meaning and purpose in a meaningless world. But there has always been another voice, both in theology and in science, though often drowned by harsher voices. Here is just one example, from the side of religion.

In the eighth chapter of Romans, Paul gives us a conception of nature as anything but complete and perfect and with it a conception of God as anything but the remote absentee landlord. Not all in the garden is lovely; neither in the garden of nature nor in the life of man. But that is precisely the sort of universe in which God can be involved.[27] 'Up to the present we know the whole created universe groans in all its parts as if in pangs of childbirth. Not only so, but even we . . . are groaning inwardly . . .' (Rom. 8.22-23). Here is recognition of struggle and cruelty and pain in nature. But it is a struggle pregnant with possibility, the possibility of new birth. It is a struggle with a hope in it. And as we read on, we see the great synthesis of Paul's imaginative thought leads him to see a parallel between nature's struggle and our own. It is a picture of unfinished man in an unfinished universe. Somehow or other both nature and man are incomplete, estranged and separated from what they could be and eventually might be.

B

I see Paul in these passages looking squarely and deeply at the facts of existence, however ugly and difficult; taking full account of them all in the meaning he seeks to discover in nature and man. And from it there does emerge a picture of God as involved, not as the dramatist who produced the play, but as player involved in the drama, feeling every feeling in a way which words cannot express. He is not the watchmaker who returns at intervals to repair the watch. He is not the remote spectator afar off. He is alongside the creation in all its processes. And what Paul sees in nature he sees in man; estranged yet with a great hope; in struggle, but it is the struggle of a new birth, the birth of a new sort of life. Is God afar off in man's struggle? No, he is alongside man, and because he is, the end is sure. The suffering is worth while. The cross-pattern is woven deeply into the texture of the whole of the creation as Paul sees it.

This is a point of view which is very different from the view of God and nature in traditional religions. But I hope to show in subsequent chapters that it is vitally relevant to the sort of world in which we live. I have merely stated it in rather stark terms at this point, without giving any reasons why we should give it our serious attention.

We must now be willing to do what Paul does: face squarely up to the facts, and be prepared to go wherever the investigation may lead, come what may. This means looking at Darwin and the century that followed. I do not think that people either inside the churches or outside have really faced up to what this should mean to our view of the universe and of God. Darwin's great protagonist, T. H. Huxley, puts it this way:

> Science seems to teach in the highest and strongest manner the great truth which is embodied in the Christian conception of entire surrender to the will of God. Sit down before the fact as a little child, be prepared to give up every preconceived notion, follow humbly wherever and to whatever abysses nature leads, or you shall learn nothing.[28]

2

DARWIN'S CENTURY

*There is grandeur in this view of life, with its several
powers, having been originally breathed by the Creator
into a few forms or into one; and that, whilst this planet
has gone cycling on according to the fixed law of gravity,
from so simple a beginning endless forms most beautiful
and most wonderful have been, and are being, evolved.*
Charles Darwin, *The Origin of Species* (2nd ed.).

THE century following the publication of *The Origin of
Species* has vindicated the main framework of Darwin's
theory. It is Darwin's century. The century is a challenge to
realism in the sense that it confronts us face to face with the
facts of the unfinished universe. These hundred years have
something tremendously important to say for our understanding of nature and of nature's God. It is quite unreal-
istic to suppose that a religion which does not take serious
account of what science has to say will command the respect
of thinking people. Those fundamentalists who still reflect
the intransigence of Philip Gosse, who opposed Darwinism
as of the devil,[1] cannot be taken seriously in any thinking
community. The traditionally orthodox who (like Mascall[2])
have examined what science has to say, but whose religion
apparently remains uninfluenced, as if science never happened, may command more of our respect. But one wonders
at the mental gymnastics required to maintain two such
separate departments of knowledge.

The implications of Darwin's century of biology for
religion has not yet been properly understood, either by the
layman or the theologian. To make a beginning, we must
first look a little more closely at what that century has had

to say. We can quite well look at Darwin and the century that followed together for a viewpoint of what is sometimes called 'neo-Darwinism'. This is the view accepted by most biologists today.

There were two parts to Darwin's theory. One was the proposition that *all living organisms are descended from one form, or a few forms, of life.* The second was a theory of the mechanism of evolution, namely, *natural selection of chance variations.*

The Continuity of Life

Biologists were far more quickly convinced about the first part than the second. The evidence for evolution is now overwhelming. Darwin provided much of it, and much more has been gathered since. Gaps there were in Darwin's story, but those gaps are being closed. The picture that emerges is one of the continuity of nature from first life to man. The living world really is a tree of life whose branches have arisen from a common trunk and are now still growing and further branching. There are still gaps in the story. But we must be amazed that they are not greater than they are, as much of the story concerns events of millions of years in the past. The most exciting gaps that modern biology is filling in are at both ends of the story, the gaps between inorganic matter and first life and between pre-man and man.

The gap between man and his immediate forebears is closing in with the discoveries being made in East Africa of tool-using pre-humans.[3] Much of the story is still tentative and is being added to at a fast rate even as the months go by. However, the evidence is such that we have a confidence in the picture of continuity of evolution from pre-man to man. Were it possible, by some act of necromancy, to resurrect our evolutionary forebears, and set them in a long line from earliest to latest, and then to review them as one might review a guard of honour, it is unlikely that we would be able to say: 'Well, here at last is a man, the creature on his left is not.' I do not believe that this continuity negates the idea of novelty, of new characters arising in man. This is an important principle. We must see how different it is from the view of those who think that the essential nature of man is preserved only if we regard his uniqueness as having no ancestry. Emil Brunner is a distinguished Protestant theologian, who accepts the evolution of man as most theologians do. He also believes in the uniqueness of man, but to him the novel features in man arose *de novo* and not out of the past.[4] He sees an unbridgeable gap between man and his forebears, though just where the gap is, between *Homo neanderthalensis* and *Homo sapiens* or some other pair, he cannot say. The distinctive characteristics of man he has called the *humanum*. The *humanum*, he says, 'is characterized by something which is entirely lacking in the animal, it possesses a dimension which is lacking in biology'. Biology knows no such unbridgeable gaps. If evolution is a continuous process, we would not expect to find any complete discontinuities in the evolutionary series from first life to man. The evidence, though we must admit its inevitable incompleteness, supports this corollary. This does not mean that novel characters do not arise. What we find at the highest level, for example, mental characters which are developed to a unique extent in man, have their rudiments in evolutionary lower forms of life.

Until 1935, there seemed to be a sharp discontinuity between the inorganic and the living. The biologist could provide a range of living creatures stretching in size all the way from a whale down to a bacterium. The chemist's range extended in the other direction from the electron-type particle through atoms to molecules, but none that approached in size the biologist's bacterium. Between the chemist's largest molecules and the biologist's smallest organisms there was a gap in size. That gap was filled in 1935 when

W. M. Stanley isolated for the first time a virus in crystal-line form. Here was something that exhibited properties of the living and the non-living. Here was something the size of the chemist's largest molecules and with the properties of life. The active part of the virus turned out to be one large molecule of deoxyribonucleic acid (in animal viruses) and ribonucleic acid (in plant viruses). The virus consisted of one such molecule surrounded by a coat of protein. On infecting an organism the virus casts off its coat and is simply a naked nucleic acid molecule. We can call it a living molecule as it has the capacity to reproduce when in the cell of a living organism. Yet in a test tube it has the appearance of a crystalline powder. Although we know virtually nothing as to how life originated, we would be well on the way if we could synthesize the DNA molecule (as it is called for short) in the laboratory. Life may have originated from one such molecule in a shallow sea of some 2,000 million years or more ago. If we could synthesize the DNA molecule in the laboratory then we would probably be well on the way to knowing something about how life first arose. As yet the patents for the process are held by nature alone.

Much modern evolutionary study is done at this molecular end of the scale. Not only is DNA a likely contender for the first living molecule, but the clue to the enormous diversity of life represented by the 500 million or more species that have existed since life began, seems to lie in the amazing nature of this molecule. The genes which are the hereditary determinants consist of DNA. Just how it is that a molecule can provide the chemical basis for life's diversity is something to which I shall return when discussing mutation of genes.

The Continuous Creation of Species

The story of evolution is not simply a record of past events. It is going on now before our eyes. The modern study of evolution is a study of a dynamic ongoing process that has never stopped, so far as we can judge. It is not a case of taking the picture of a process that has now come to a standstill. The picture is constantly changing. Every time an insect becomes resistant to a new man-made insecticide, or when a bacterium becomes resistant to a new antibiotic, we witness evolutionary change. The locomotive of evolution moves much faster than Darwin ever dared to dream. We can measure its rate over matters of one or a few generations. For fruit flies this is a matter of weeks, for bacteria of hours. Fifty years ago it may have been true to say that no man had ever witnessed evolution. Today many of us witness evolution day by day in our laboratories. By the nature of the case, the changes which we can observe over short periods are mostly changes within the species and not transformations of one species into another. The anti-evolutionist is quick to point this out and commonly adds that man has never witnessed the transformation of one species into another. The contrary is true. The plant *Raphanobrassica* is famous because it was the first species produced by man from two pre-existing species.[5] It is completely fertile, but quite infertile with either parent species. By any definition it is a good new species. There are now dozens of such cases amongst plants. It is, of course, a relatively rare experience for man to witness the production of a new species. In the normal course of events that is something that takes millions of years to complete.

The panorama that modern evolutionary theory presents is one of a continuity of transformation of first life over some 2,000 millions of years into some 500 million or more species, most of them now extinct. There is good indirect evidence that it all stemmed from something which might have resembled the viruses we know today. At the very heart of the enduring nature of nature is change and instability. It was Darwin who gave us the clue to how the changes were wrought.

The Role of Chance in Change

Darwin's theory of how organisms had evolved was accepted much less readily than the fact that organisms had evolved. His evidence for the theory of natural selection of chance variation was circumstantial and indirect. To that extent it was unconvincing. The science of genetics had not yet come into existence and the key to the validity of the theory of natural selection lay in its hands. Yet curiously enough, geneticists remained completely sceptical until the late 1920's. The reasons were numerous. It is perhaps enough to say here that the early genetical theories of evolution were too crude to be convincing. The last three decades have seen quite an amazing development of the theory of natural selection in the light of genetics. These studies have proceeded along many lines from the most esoteric mathematical arguments initiated in 1930 by Sir Ronald Fisher[6] and Professor Sewall Wright[7] to direct observations of natural selection in the laboratory and in nature.

A modern neo-Darwinist would frame the theory of natural selection of chance variation somewhat as follows. The source of Darwin's chance variations, the building blocks of evolution, are now known to be mutations of genes. Mutation is a spontaneous change of the chemical structure of the hereditary determinants or genes which are made of DNA. You are what you are, that is to say *Homo sapiens* with black hair, an aquiline nose, blue eyes and so on, by virtue of the particular complement of genes in each of the hundred billion or so cells that constitute your body. There may be a thousand genes in each of your cells. The complement you have is unique (unless you have an identical twin). No one has your collection though your relatives will share some of the same genes. Compared with you and me, first life may have been simply one naked gene, certainly not many such units. Now, all the millions of different sorts of genes that go to make the difference between all the organisms that are and have ever been, have arisen by the reproduction of the original gene, plus spontaneous change in the process of gene reproduction. We now know that the number of the sorts of such mutational changes is astronomically large. This is possible because of the special structure of the nucleic acid molecule. And every different gene produces different sorts of chemical messengers which have the end result of producing some different quality in the organism that possesses them. Life was not made with static qualities, but the very basic molecule of life was endowed from the first with enormous potentialities of change. The causes of these changes are unknown. The effects are clear.

Is the direction of change of a gene related to the needs of the organism? If an animal moves into a cold climate, will the mutations be such as to cause the animal to be resistant to cold? That would seem to be a logical enough idea, but it is not what happens. The sorts of mutations that occur are completely unrelated to the needs of the organisms at the time they occur. Indeed, most mutations are deleterious to the organism. The dread disease haemophilia, or bleeding, in man is due to the mutation of a gene for normal blood clotting to one for haemophilia. The genes in our bodies may be normal for blood clotting, but in the sex cells of every man about two in every 100,000 contain a newly mutated gene for haemophilia. So this gives the chance a man has of giving this mutant gene to his offspring. If most mutations are deleterious, how is it ever possible that mutation can be the basis of creative evolution? The answer briefly is that adaptive evolution is dependent upon the few mutations that do happen to be beneficial. They are few in relation to the deleterious ones, but when we add them up over countless aeons in countless organisms the absolute number of beneficial mutations becomes enormous. The picture we have to visualize is one of an enormous potential for change in the genes, potential for change in all sorts of directions. With this unlimited resource resident in the molecular structure of the gene and given unlimited time, the enormous diversity of life has arisen on this earth.

This is only part of the story. It is one thing to have all sorts of building blocks from which an elaborate house can be built. It is another to build the house. The builder, said Darwin, is natural selection. The resistance of insects to DDT is an example. In some cases the resistance is conferred by the mutation of a single gene which alters the insect's capacity to deal chemically with the poison. Now the amazing thing is that all the evidence points to the view that mutation for DDT resistance has been going on before DDT was ever invented. All that DDT does is to 'select' those organisms that happen to possess the mutation and kill the rest. In the days before DDT, there was no advantage in being resistant to it. Now there is, and those insects that contain the mutant gene survive and reproduce, the others perish. This illustrates two important points. Mutation to DDT resistance occurs quite independently of DDT and secondly, it points to the enormous potential for gene mutation. Presumably these same insects are even now producing mutant genes that one day may protect them against some chemical at present not invented. These mutations have to await their opportunity if ever it comes. So in natural selection, those genes persist which confer some adaptive advantage for survival and reproduction on the organism that possesses them. Borrowing a phrase from Herbert Spencer, Darwin called this 'survival of the fittest'. We prefer not to use this phrase now as it conveys an idea of a life and death struggle. Much of evolution is so gentle as to be almost imperceptible; some small advantage is being added here and another there that gives the individual some slight advantage over its brothers and sisters.

The idea of chance mutation and the idea of natural selection have both been heavy targets for anti-evolutionist fire. The adjective 'chance' has a special meaning, namely that the sort of mutation that occurs at any time is quite unrelated to the needs of the organism at that time. By chance, one or more may turn out to be useful, just because the potential for mutation is so enormous. Mutation is random or 'chance' in relation to the needs of the organism at the time it occurs. There is a hit-and-miss aspect to mutation. Furthermore, at the chemical level, mutation of the gene is an accident in reproduction of the DNA molecule that constitutes the gene. A million times the gene may reproduce exact copies of itself, but the million and first may not be exact, there has been a failure of exact replication. This is mutation. It is the cause of all that is useful in evolution as well as much that is deleterious. The gene for haemophilia is an example of one of many very deleterious mutations in man; others cause idiocy, others premature death. Dobzhansky[3] lists five pages of human diseases which are known to be due to gene mutation in man. These are the facts of life as much as an earthquake or anything else that causes untold suffering and pain. If you want God to be directly responsible for mutations, then you must include these in your list as well as the ones that may produce the genius. I have stressed this aspect of evolutionary change because I think it is essential that any philosophy or theology of nature take account of what seems to be sheer accident, random or chance events. They exist. Moreover, they provide a clue which we shall develop later. In his excellent history of evolutionary thought, the historian Greene points out that the element of chance in the Darwinian theory appealed to the American philosophers Charles Peirce and William James 'as a means of deliverance from the mechanical determinism of nineteenth-century physics and chemistry'.[8]

The principle of natural selection is subject to much misunderstanding. The haphazard production of enormous variation and enormous numbers of animals and plants in the hope that here and there one may turn out to be better fitted for life and selected out from the rest seems unworthy of an ordered universe. Does it not stretch the imagination just too far to suppose that the human eye in all its complexities could be the product of the bringing together of so many useful and necessary elements all at once? Unless all the parts were there it would not work. You do not make a clock without a spring. You need the spring and everything else before it will work. Does not natural selection demand an orderly sequence and coincidence of variation seem so improbable as to be impossible? As soon imagine a million monkeys banging away at random on a million typewriters chancing to produce one of Shakespeare's plays!

Macneile Dixon said in his Gifford lectures that for evolution to have proceeded in this way is as incredible as to suppose the production of a great picture by a blind painter sprinkling a canvas at random with a brush dipped in unseen colours.[9] The analogy is false. No competent evolutionist has ever proposed such a ridiculous concept. It reveals a complete misunderstanding of the nature of selection as operating over countless generations. If we were to use this analogy at all, we would have to reword it something like this. Not one, but a million, indeed billions, of blind painters each sprinkle a few splashes of colour on millions of canvases. Of these, only the few that show the feeblest suggestion of a meaningful picture are preserved; the rest are destroyed. The selected rudimentary pictures are reproduced a millionfold. Again millions of blind painters add a few random touches of paint here and there. Again the best pictures are selected and reproduced, and so on millions of times, corresponding to the number of generations that have elapsed since life began. This analogy is much closer to what selection is, but it is still too crude to convey the modern meaning of selection of chance variation. Despite its indirectness and colossal waste, it does produce a coherence and integration of the organism minutely adapted to its environment. Given enormous potentiality, changes good and bad, struggle, death, enormous loss in the face of unpredictable circumstances and reproduction, there do emerge organisms endowed with the requisites necessary to conquer every corner of the world. This is the nature of the creative process.

Dobzhansky has compared the whole process to the production of a work of art.[10] Both sorts of creation involve the risk of ending in failure. Without the possibility of this risk, there would be no creation. Evolution is a creative process. It could never be called that if it were simply the unfolding of completely preordained pathways. There is no creation in a completely deterministic system. Sir Ronald Fisher has written that, 'It was Darwin's chief contribution not only to biology but to the whole of natural science, to have brought to light a process by which contingencies *a priori* impossible, are given, in the process of time, an increasing probability, until it is the non-occurrence rather than their occurrence which becomes highly improbable'.[11] We are presented then with a picture of reasonable credibility of a process that involves elements of chance and aspects of disorder with a fairly mechanical sorting-out process accounting for much of this order. Much more can be found in Dobzhansky's book,[3] and in other modern works, of the numerous subtleties of the modern genetical theory of natural selection which give a sense of verisimilitude to the theory that earlier formulations failed to give. We should not still do battle on ancient ground. The simple accounts of the past were too simple to be credible.

Most of us seem to want the process of evolution to be more direct than it is. But there is no evidence to support the popular misconception that environment directly induces the sorts of mutations that the organism needs for that environment. The role of environment is to select, not to direct, the nature of change. Nor is there any evidence for, nor necessity to postulate, any internal directing agency to mutation. There is no need for that because of the enormous potential for gene change, and the enormous potentiality for different expressions of genes under different circumstances. The expression of the gene varies with the environment. Knowledge of the details of this has led Waddington to develop an important supplement to the theory of natural selection which he calls genetic assimilation.[12, 13] An animal develops callouses on its feet when it lives in rough terrain. Some do so more effectively than others because of their genetic constitution. Natural selection favours those whose genetic constitution disposes them to react usefully in this way. It will gradually result in a race in which the development of the useful character has been taken over by the genes so that they produce it even in the absence of special help from the environment. I mention this somewhat technical detail because it makes the point that natural selection is more subtle than its critics usually imagine. When we first come to consider the origin of complex adaptive organs such as the human eye, our initial reaction is like Darwin's when he contemplated the wonder of its design: 'The eye to this day gives me a cold shudder.' In the light of a modern understanding of natural selection, many of these difficulties are removed.[14, 15]

Order and Purpose?

The order which we witness in nature has involved a history in which there are elements of randomness, chaos, waste, disaster and struggle. From apparent disorder there does emerge order. The picture bears no resemblance to the one with which we started, of a static contrivance made and driven by an infallible engineer, and made according to preordained blueprints. The evolution of species looks more like a vast experiment in which the outcome at any stage seems unpredictable; as unpredictable as the details of history. There have been shortlived failures and longlived successes; there have been blind alleys; sudden vast explosions of some types only to collapse again. The dinosaurs of the Mesozoic were extravaganzas in size and mass, beyond the power of a nervous system to manage and co-ordinate. They perished for what they were, monstrosities of nature. If the complete details are unpredictable, then it is also true that the details are unrepeatable.[16] What is alive today, has the history of the past built into it. It would be as impossible to repeat biological history as to repeat the history of Julius Caesar in exact detail. Evolution has been opportunistic at every step, in the sense that what survives depends entirely on circumstance at the time, and circumstance changes without warning. Environment is a kaleidoscope of change. Organisms must change with it or perish. The essence of capacity to survive is capacity to change. As life lasts, evolution has no end.

What of the future? So far as man is concerned, the evolutionary story took on a new aspect when he appeared on the scene. The same principles that applied to all creatures applied to him, but a new one was added. With the rise of man, there emerged what Dobzhansky[16] and Huxley[17] have called *cultural* evolution. Culture is what man learns from his neighbour, and what he therefore transmits, not by heredity, but by learning, and through the medium of language. It is this inherited information and 'know-how' that has given man the capacity to determine the direction of his own evolution. Living beings other than man become adapted to their environment by changing their genes. Man does this but he does more, he becomes adapted chiefly now by invention, in other words, by changing his culture. As soon as evolution produced a creature who could build up an inheritance of learned traditions, the course of evolution took a new direction. In a sense the creature now had the power to control its course. Man knows two sorts of inheritance, genetic and cultural, innate and learned. Man's genotype is such as to make the development of culture possible, whereas that of the ape is not. Man's two inheritances have

meant the difference between life in the jungle and civilization. It is we who shape the world. All other creatures are
shaped by the world. Man has the power to determine his
own destiny on this planet. This is his birthright. In the
words of Genesis 1.28, he has 'dominion over the fish of
the sea, and over the fowl of the air, and over every living
thing that moveth upon the earth'.

To claim that with the rise of man a new feature enters
into the evolutionary story is not to deny the existence of a
modicum of cultural inheritance in other animals. The
capacity to learn by experience goes all the way back to the
flat worms.[18] The capacity to communicate what is learned
is quite strongly developed in social insects, such as bees,
and in social birds and mammals. There are rudiments of
language in non-human animals. But man is the only creature who has a highly developed capacity for symbolic
thought and for the use of language, and who has built up a
complex body of traditions known as culture. The capacity
for using language is found in animals other than man in
only rudimentary form. The capacity is given to man by his
hereditary endowment. The ability to speak a language is a
matter of genes. Which language, is almost certainly a
matter of culture.

Acquired cultural characters are transmitted by learning.
Acquired bodily characters are not. So culture is more
easily modifiable than is biological heredity. With this
capacity man can adapt himself from a stone age to a
bronze, and in these latter days to an atomic age.

The importance of cultural evolution in man has led some
to ask the question: has natural selection ceased in man?
The answer to this question is complex, for natural selection
has been relaxed in some directions, and intensified in
others. It has certainly not stopped.[3]

The story as I have told it is mechanical through and
through, because this is the aspect of nature that science is
so skilled in revealing. Does this then mean that nature is a

machine that makes itself? Is there no place for purpose and ultimate meaning? Some biologists say that this is where the story ends. But there are others who see this as the outer aspect of the history of nature, a very real aspect but not the whole aspect. The distinguished geneticist Sewall Wright says, 'Science deliberately accepts a rigorous limitation of its activities to the description of the external aspect of events. In carrying out this program, the scientist should not, however, deceive himself or others into thinking that he is giving an account of all of reality. The unique inner creative aspect of every event escapes him.'[19] This statement bears a striking resemblance to Teilhard de Chardin's concept of the 'within of things'. Writing of evolution, he says: 'I am convinced that the two points of view require to be brought into union, and that they soon will unite in a kind of phenomenology or generalized physic in which the internal aspects of things as well as the external aspect of the world will be taken into account.' 'To write the true natural history of the world, we should need to be able to follow it from within.'[20] Hartshorne speaks of the 'matter' way and the 'mind' way of describing reality.[21] The material mode, he says, is that part of the complete mode which is capable of scientific precision. Much depends upon seeing that the 'complete mode' does not exclude any scientific procedure. It merely opens our eyes to the 'beyond'—the 'beyond' which tends to escape any save a vague, intuitive apprehension.

3

CHANCE AND PURPOSE

I own that I cannot see as plainly as others do, and as I should wish to do, evidence of design and beneficence on all sides of us. There seems to me too much misery in the world. I cannot persuade myself that a beneficent and omnipotent God would have designedly created the Ichneumonidae with the express intention of their feeding within the living bodies of Caterpillars, or that a cat would play with mice. Not believing this, I see no necessity in the belief that the eye was expressly designed. On the other hand, I cannot anyhow be contented to view this wonderful universe, and especially the nature of man, and to conclude that everything is the result of brute force. . . .

I cannot think that the world as we see it is the result of chance; and yet I cannot look at each separate thing as the result of design . . . I am, and shall ever remain, in a hopeless muddle.

If anything is designed, certainly man must be, yet I cannot admit that man's rudimentary mammae were designed . . . I am in a thick mud yet I cannot keep out of the question.

Charles Darwin in letters to Asa Gray, 1860.[1]

The Idea of God after Darwin

IN the quotations that head this chapter, we find Darwin making two mental lists, one of them contains such marvels as the human eye and the mind of man, the other stinging wasps, carnivorous beasts, functionless male nipples and the like. One list seems to suggest a beneficent design in nature, the other argues against it. In a letter to Sir J. D. Hooker in 1856 he said: 'What a devil's chaplain might write on the clumsy, wasteful, blundering, low and horribly cruel works of nature!'[1] Darwin could not keep the problems raised by these lists out of his restless mind. Is nature a product of purpose and design, or is it the outcome of chance? The quotations come from letters written to the American botanist, Asa Gray, who was both a Darwinist and a deist. He contended that the theory of natural selection simply altered the manner in which God's design in nature must be conceived, but did not destroy the argument for design itself.[2] The same proposition was made later by Bishop Frederick Temple in 1884 in his claim that Darwinism did not affect Paley's argument, but only the details of how the blueprint was turned into a creation.[3] Darwin was at first attracted by Gray's argument, as is indicated by the title he provided for the English version of one of Gray's essays, *Natural Selection not Inconsistent with Natural Theology*.[4]

That Gray was thoroughly confused, Darwin was soon to discover. The argument of the deists was the watch–watchmaker analogy of William Paley. Darwin was, as we have seen, familiar with it. Two of the quotations opposite the title page of *The Origin of Species* were from theological works, one from the *Bridgewater Treatises* and the other from Bishop Butler. Darwin came to see that the facts of natural selection of chance variation did not fit that picture of nature at all. Gray asks him, 'But how could chance produce design?' He wanted Darwin to replace the idea of chance variation with some sort of directed change; the direction to be beneficial. A watch, he said, can be changed to produce a better watch, a series of appropriately directed changes could convert it into a chronometer. But the whole point of Darwin's thesis was that variations were *not* directed; some were beneficial and some were deleterious. If perchance some were beneficial then the organism that possessed them had a greater chance of surviving and multiplying. Every step of Gray's argument led backwards into all the hopeless difficulties of Paley's picture of a perfect nature and divine mechanic. Darwin rejected it.

As if in a last ditch stand, Gray asked Darwin what would convince him of 'cosmic design'. In a reply written on September 17, 1861, Darwin said that the question was a 'poser'. He tried to imagine experiences that would be convincing, but gave up the effort as 'childish', as indeed it was.[2] Gray's question presupposes God to be a thing besides others within the universe of existing things. It is quite legitimate to ask the question if such a thing does exist. But the answer is also justified that it does not exist. Gray was no more help to Darwin in his muddle than the Church is to perplexed youth of today, when in the name of the Christian religion preachers offer that sort of conception of God. It is completely irrelevant, there is no evidence for it, and it is remote from the meaning of God in the New Testament. This is the dead hand of the past against which Bishop John A. T. Robinson so effectively argued in his book *Honest to God*. Charles Kingsley saw the issue clearly at the time and wrote, 'Now they have got rid of an interfering God—a master-magician as I call it—they have to choose between the absolute empire of accident and a living, immanent, ever-working God.'[5]

Darwinism did something very decisive for religion. It cleared the air. T. H. Huxley pointed this out soon after the first storms of controversy had passed. He said that the fundamental problems of a philosophy of life and of the universe existed in the pre-Darwin era. They still exist in the post-Darwin era. Darwin did not answer the questions raised by philosophy. But he did create a situation which means that 'the present generation has the advantage of being better provided with the means of freeing itself from the tyranny of certain solutions.'[1] This is a perpetual role that science has played for religion. It helps to identify and remove the accumulated overburden that hides the gold.

Is Mechanism Enough?

There is no evidence that Darwin was ever confronted

with any alternative to the supernaturalist God of deism. To the questions he asked about chance and purpose he got no answers to his dying day. That is now our problem. It can be formulated as a question: Is life to be interpreted wholly in terms of the mechanistic theory of the universe? If it is, then we must conclude with the biologist Bentley Glass: 'Natural selection . . . produces a semblance of purposiveness in the causal chains, though there has been only a blind, purposeless agency at work.'[6] Similarly, the distinguished evolutionist G. G. Simpson writes, 'Man is the result of a purposeless and materialistic process. . . .'[7]

This is a conclusion that many scientists and laymen alike draw from Darwinism. For them, Darwin completes the story begun by the cosmologists of the sixteenth and seventeenth centuries, but with a difference; by the nineteenth century, God had been disposed of, that is to say, the sort of God who was supposed to have made the mechanism. It must be conceded that if living organisms can be interpreted wholly in terms of the mechanistic theory of nature, then there is no room for concepts of purpose and God. The deists failed to see this. They argued for purpose in a mechanical universe on the grounds that things seem to be constructed to serve useful ends. The proof of 'divine goodness' according to William Paley rested on the proposition that 'in a vast plurality of instances in which contrivance is perceived, the design of the contrivance is beneficial'. But this is not, as Paley contended, an argument for a purposive universe. Natural selection explains the fact that adaptations of plants and animals serve useful ends. The sense of purpose, upon which deism depended, was 'explained away' by Darwin. A concept of purpose in the universe that is to have any validity must be more profound than that. A machine performs a useful end, it is designed to that end, but it is not purposive. A purposive system is one that cannot be described solely in terms of the mechanical relation of its parts, the power that drives the parts.

When I perform a conscious purposive act such as writing, my whole action cannot be understood solely in terms of the mechanics of writing. In addition, one must take into account the end or purpose I have in mind. There is a mental component to my action which is the purpose I have in mind when I set pen to paper. That purpose is a real cause of what I do. My action is purposive. To call something purposive simply because it serves useful ends is to run into the confusion that deism created and still creates. Even to this day, deism casts its long shadow over much of our thinking about God. It is like the fall-out that clings long after the explosion is past.

Another mistake we commonly fall into is to suppose that a denial of the mechanistic theory of the universe and the plea for a purposive interpretation is a denial of mechanical aspects to nature. It is nothing of the sort. What it denies is that the entities of the universe, be they electrons or men, are 100 per cent automata. I used the word in the exact sense that Kapp has defined automata, namely, self-constructing, self-operating, self-repairing, self-maintaining machines.[8] Some machines are not 100 per cent automata; an automatic gear-change vehicle is more so than a manual gear-change vehicle. The mechanistic theory is the theory that all entities in this universe are complete automata; they are completely closed systems as distinct from open systems which require some input from outside the machine. This is the issue. I am not arguing as to whether or not machines serve useful ends. That is irrelevant, and because it is irrelevant, the deists eventually found they had no argument. *The issue is whether or not the universe and all that is in it are to be interpreted as 100 per cent automata.* This is what I mean by mechanism.

In the mechanistic view the smallest things like electrons and the big things like solar systems and the in-between things like men are, every one of them, 100 per cent automata. The ideal of mechanism is the reductionist programme of subdividing the universe into its component bits, the dozen or so elementary particles of the physicist. Having subdivided the universe into the nearest to nothing as possible, the mechanist proceeds to build up a whole cosmology. The bigger things like trees and men are simply rearrangements of the smaller things with lots of space in between. But whether large or small, they are self-regulating, self-constructing machines. This is sometimes called the physico-chemical interpretation of the universe. Physics and chemistry become, in this view, the fundamental sciences. Concepts of purpose and value and mind and God are quite irrelevant in this scheme. There may appear to be sets of qualities in the mechanical universe such as smell, taste, colour and other qualities that we experience in sensations and feelings, but these are only appearances. They are epiphenomena, like the ticking of the clock, and of no more relevance than that. In another analogy they are 'ghosts in the machine'. I am using the word 'feeling' as one of the threefold fundamental traits of mind: 'feeling', 'knowing' and 'willing'.

> Feeling (in the usual technical sense) and sensation are the two main forms of sheer intuition or having of qualities, willing is acting or striving with regard to them, knowing is using them as signs of something beyond themselves, as instances of a class or the like.[9]

In the mechanistic theory of nature my feelings and sensations are side effects like the ticking of the clock, and of no more relevance than that.

The mechanistic theory has never been proved. When it is believed, it is by act of faith. But apart from this, the universe does not seem to be constructed to the end of being so easily understood.*

* For detailed criticism of an exclusively mechanistic interpretation of mind see J. Beloff, *The Existence of Mind* (Macgibbon and Kee, London, 1962) and I. T. Ramsey, *Religion and Science* (SPCK., London, 1964), ch. 2.

The Real Relevance of Mechanism

Scientists are conditioned by their training to think in the categories of mechanism. There are good reasons for this. Many of the workings of nature are analogous to machines and can be profitably analysed as such. No one would wish to deny that William Harvey furthered our understanding of the circulatory system when he described it in terms of pumps and valves and principles of hydraulics. The flow of blood certainly obeys the rules of hydraulics. Nor should we wish to deny that neuro-physiology may have been advanced by comparing the brain with an electronic computer. But this is no justification for making mechanism an all-embracing view of the universe. It does not follow that mechanical models of nature exhaust the nature of nature.

As we have already seen, Descartes more than anyone else made the doctrine of mechanism explicit. In so doing, he most certainly advanced the experimental study of nature. It brought out into the open those aspects of the living world that could be subjected to the experimental analysis, and so opened up a way to more accurate description. It did not provide man with new instruments of investigation, but with a way of looking at nature that made analysis possible. When living things were depicted as machines, new possibilities were opened up in formulating hypotheses as to how they might work. Mention has also been made in Chapter 1 of some biologists who were clearly influenced in this way by Descartes. However, it is one thing to study nature as though it were a machine—which is an empirically useful approach. It is quite another to pronounce the dogma that nature *is* a machine. This is what Descartes did in his *Traité de l'Homme* (1664). Dingle put the issue clearly when he wrote:

It is very questionable whether the great advances of those two centuries following Descartes could have been possible without the simple concrete picture of a passive extended universe of matter presented for study to independent minds. There was much to be done that could be effectively conceived in those terms and the acceptance of an over-confident materialism was, perhaps, not too high a price to pay for the discussions and correlations that would have been achieved, if at all, only with much more difficulty, less general understanding, and far less speed. It was not until almost our own time that the Cartesian doctrine began to mislead. . . . Physics today is in a transition stage in which many of its devotees, rather than abandon the Cartesian universe, are prepared to make nonsense by giving it contradictory properties. . . . It is perhaps a melancholy thought that we can best celebrate the death of Descartes (three centuries ago) by expediting the death of his system.[10]

Archbishop William Temple used even stronger words: 'If I were asked what was the most disastrous moment in the history of Europe I should be strongly tempted to answer that it was the period of leisure when René Descartes, having no claims to meet, remained for a whole day "shut up alone in a stove".'[11] He was referring to the habit of thought established by Descartes which penetrated into the thinking of science, philosophy, politics and economics; the division of the universe into two separate and disparate realms, spirit and matter, mind and body, nature and God. His was not a universe but a diverse, split from top to bottom by this two-substance doctrine of nature. It was a simple subsequent step to toss out the spirit-substance as irrelevant to the system, as indeed it was, and to leave behind stark mechanism, which is what happened. The death of Descartes' system, which Dingle proposes should be expedited, would be the death of the mechanistic theory of nature in which all entities large or small are complete automata or collections of automata.

The supporters of the mechanistic theory of nature fail to understand the nature of science, which is to abstract from nature. The abstractions of science are pictures of reality, and not reality. The concepts of the electron and the living cell are models of what these parts of reality may be like. There is no general agreement amongst philosophers of science as to the relation between the model and reality. An appropriate analogy is one that Toulmin[12] uses: the theory or picture of science is like a map. A map of Sydney is not Sydney. It tells us a lot about Sydney, and it leaves out a lot about Sydney. If it is a street map, it will tell us nothing about the topography or the vegetation. We will need quite a lot of different sorts of maps if we are to get closer to what Sydney is. Maps are rough at first. They can be improved. The same is true of theories in science, be they theories of the electron or of the cell. And just as we may need more than one map to get any sort of picture of Sydney, so too we may need more than one sort of map to get around the electron or the cell. The universal model of science is the machine. Science uses the machine as its picture of reality. But if we then say that reality is therefore a machine, we mistake the picture for reality. It is to commit what Whitehead called 'the fallacy of misplaced concreteness'.[13] So Wordsworth wrote:

> Sweet is the lore which Nature brings;
>   Our meddling intellect
> Mis-shapes the beauteous forms of things;
>   We murder to dissect.
> Enough of science and of art:
>   Close up these barren leaves;
> Come forth, and bring with you a heart
>   That watches and receives.[14]

We do not need to condemn science because it does not grapple with the whole nature of things. Science and its mechanistic analysis provide a view of one aspect of nature. The poet warns that this is not the whole of nature. Bergson put the issue in a rather more balanced way when he wrote: 'The forceps of our mind are crude and they crush the delicacy of reality when we attempt to hold it.'

The proponents of the mechanistic theory of nature have taken heed of Whitehead's injunction, 'seek simplicity . . .', but they have not heeded the rest of the sentence which ran, 'and distrust it'.[13] The theory is certainly simple and has worked up to a point. But unknown to many of its constant users, it is beginning to outlive its usefulness. It is still the accepted article of faith of most of those biologists in the world today who take the trouble to make their position known. It is much less widely held by physicists and chemists. I shall maintain that despite its great usefulness as a proposition about nature, it is positively misleading and completely inadequate when regarded as saying all that has to be said about nature.

The extreme reaction of the 'vitalists' of the nineteenth century was a mistake in the opposite direction. Because mechanism did not account for all, there was no need to postulate a mystical 'life force' to control life, as did Bergson, Driesch and others. That argument has now been convincingly discredited by many biologists and philosophers, and by none more effectively than by Woodger.[15]

We have now passed beyond the stage when over-simplification had some advantages, when we could present alternative propositions either mechanism or vitalism, either purpose or chance. I shall argue for the 'both/and' position—that there is a mechanical aspect to nature which is the outer view, and that there is an inner aspect of nature less amenable to mechanical analysis. Similarly, we do not have to deny purpose when we discover that there is room in the universe for accident and chance events. I shall argue for a role of chance in a purposive universe. The alternative is virtually complete mechanical determinism, for which I find no evidence.

An Alternative to Complete Mechanism

What, then, is the basis for proposing an alternative to the mechanistic theory of nature? One could argue that the physicists are now finding that mechanism does not fit their world of electrons and atoms as neatly as they once thought. There are many physicists who would agree, amongst them Bohr and Heisenberg.[16] Or one might argue that the biologists are now finding that the theory does not work as well as they once thought. As an empirical statement about modern biologists, this would not be true. Biologists are about as mechanistic as they ever were, so one might then have to argue that most biologists are just misguided, and that also may be true. We shall have to return to physics and biology, but they are not suitable starting points. It is not primarily because some physicists or some biologists have decided that the mechanistic theory of nature is outmoded that we seek an alternative to mechanism. This could be a reason, but it is certainly not the prime reason. Although I agree with much that Coulson has to say about science and religion, I disagree when he says that science is a religious activity. He seems to argue from science for the validity of religious beliefs about God and man. The argument, he says, 'leads us stage by stage through natural theology to Christian belief. We must begin with natural theology.'[17] I beg to differ. We must begin, not with the electron nor the amoeba nor the universe, but with man. At this point I find myself in complete agreement with Raven's approach to meaning in the universe.[18]

The most directly accessible clue we have to the nature of the universe is neither the electron, nor amoeba, but man. What is man? That is the relevant question to ask. It is man's self-awareness that leads him to ask this question. His answer determines his answer to the broader question that includes it, what is the nature and purpose of the universe? Streeter once remarked, 'I have had experiences that materialism cannot explain'.[19] That is the point. What matters to me mostly is not mass, velocity and the like, but my own experience of value and purpose, all the qualities of friendship and love. It is precisely these qualities that the mechanistic theory of nature leaves out. Galileo called them the secondary qualities and because they could not be measured, he did not regard them as real. 'It seems an extremely unfortunate arrangement', said Whitehead, 'that we should perceive a lot of things that are not there. Yet that is what the theory of secondary qualities in fact comes to. . . . We may not pick and choose. For us the red glow of the sunset should be as much a part of nature as are the molecules and electric waves by which men of science would explain the phenomenon.'[20] Our difficulty is to exhibit the redness of the sunset on one system of thought with the electromagnetic waves and the agitation of molecules connected with it. That is one of our problems. Because this is difficult, are we to ignore it, or to be completely sceptical that there is anything but a mechanical side to nature? We are inclined to over-scepticism. William Temple remarked to Bertrand Russell that he believed in life after death more strongly than the evidence really warranted, to which Bertrand Russell was said to have replied that he disbelieved it much more than the evidence warranted.[21]

In the mechanistic view of nature, colour, sound, aesthetic and moral quality are no longer in nature, they are side effects but no more. Yet these are the most real experiences to me as a person. I am immediately aware of experiences of value and to that extent I 'know' what courage, forgiveness, hope and other values are. I 'know' existentially, though my theoretical formulations about them may be quite vague. There is an existential side to my experience and also a cognitive one. But they do not necessarily advance step by step together. We do not have to interpret the world before we experience it. But those experiences that do matter to me cannot be excluded when I do come to seek an answer to the question—what is man? If an amoeba could write about the universe it knew, it would presumably not be able to include an account of the universe man knows, and, to that extent, if not in other ways, its world view would be inadequate. Nor could I accept a view of the universe that was written from the basis of what sodium chloride appears to be in a chemist's laboratory, even though this might be a most exhaustive chemical analysis of the salt. If there are such things in the world as purposes which make things as they are have their meaning beyond them, of values not yet realized and of freedom to choose, they cannot be dealt with by a method which looks exclusively to 'what is lower for the manifestation of the higher'.[22] The principle I am proposing is the opposite, that the lower be interpreted in terms of the higher.[23]

This is the basis of the great attempt of the process philosophers, notably among them Whitehead and Hartshorne, to provide an alternative to sheer mechanism. It is the qualitative content of human lives, the potentiality of this aspect of life which we might call moral, aesthetic and spiritual that is the basis of their view. From their evaluation of man and his experiences they proceed to interpret the rest of the universe and not *vice versa*. The one cannot be done without the other. This approach has a great tradition in Christian thought all the way from Origen in the third century.[24] In our own time, we find in this tradition of thought theologians such as Farmer[25] and Raven. For example, Raven says, 'Despite our consciousness of frustration and sin it is in mankind, in the son of man, if any such deserves to be singled out, that we must surely apprehend and appreciate the character of the universe'.[26] I take it to be the approach of Teilhard de Chardin, whose book on the evolution of the cosmos is appropriately entitled *The Phenomenon of Man*. This is essentially a religious work set in a scientific framework. It is not, as some reviewers have tended to assume, a religion argued from science. In the same vein, another theologian, Woods, writes: 'If we ignore the primacy of our personal being as the source and spring of our ultimate means of explanation, we are bound to find the world increasingly obscure. We shall be attempting to explain our personal life in impersonal terms which are less plain than what they should explain.'[27]

Alternative approaches have been made by theologians. The cosmological 'proofs' of God argued by St Thomas Aquinas are of this nature. They have proved to be exceedingly vulnerable. Nearer our own time, Tennant made a famous but unsuccessful attempt to refine the argument from design in nature direct to God.[28] The point of view I am arguing is for a double approach through the inner life of feeling of self and through our cognitive understanding of the cosmos, but starting with self and never neglecting it. This approach has not received nearly enough attention in recent thinking. Tillich is a notable exception amongst present-day theologians; in his later writings especially, he includes the scientific view of nature in his synthesis. His broad canvas is the whole of culture and religion.[29] An earlier theological expression of this principle is William Temple's *Nature, Man and God*. In discussing the basis for belief in the ultimate spiritual nature of the universe and the initiative of spirit, Temple said: 'It is doubtful whether it would be possible in the long run to hold to these two convictions with any assurance apart from the third, which presses itself rather as a matter of direct experience than as intellectual conviction; this is the reality of intercourse and fellowship between the spirit of man and the supreme Spirit.'

This was the light that Tennyson discovered as he sought to rebuild the universe on a surer foundation than his age had given him:

> *I found Him not in world or sun,*
> *Or eagle's wing, or insect's eye,*
> *Nor thro' the questions men may try,*
> *The petty cobwebs we have spun:*

If e'er when faith had fall'n asleep,
I heard a voice 'believe no more'
And heard an ever-breaking shore
That tumbled in the Godless deep:

A warmth within the breasts would melt
The freezing reason's colder part,
And like a man in wrath the heart
Stood up and answer'd 'I have felt'.[30]

So too with Wordsworth:

And I have felt
A presence that disturbs me with the joy
Of elevated thoughts; a sense sublime
Of something far more deeply interfused,
. . . and in the mind of man
A motion and a spirit, that impels
All thinking things, all objects of all thought,
And rolls through all things. . . .[31]

Neither theologian nor poet is urging that we replace the sure knowledge of science with vague feelings within. The question before us is whether we can hold together the accurate knowledge of science and the inner 'knowledge' or feelings we have, be they aesthetic, moral or spiritual, call them what you will. This approach does not exclude any scientific analysis, but, as Hartshorne has said, it 'opens our eyes to the beyond that tends to escape any save a vague, intuitive apprehension. No exact analysis or observation in physical or spatio-temporal terms is forbidden, but rather we are enabled consciously to experience the world both with all possible accuracy and with the dim background (which, consciously or not, is always there anyway) of invincibly indefinite feeling for the "life of things" (Wordsworth). In the end, this consciousness may actually increase the extent of our accurate knowledge, and it is sure to increase our enjoyment of the world, peace of mind and understanding of ourselves.'[32] We get something of this feeling for the wholeness of things in the beautiful writings of the biologist Agnes Arber, when she says that to explain a theory 'is to think it in terms of the whole', and adds that biology is intelligible in physico-chemical terms though not explicable in these terms.[33] We require at this level a notion of explanation that has a greater richness of content than one that has been prearranged for the inanimate world. Another biologist, Thorpe, expressed the same view when he concluded his book on *Biology and the Nature of Man* with these words:

> Moreover, when we consider the coherence of knowledge in all its aspects, the scientific world picture appears less and less convincing as a complete account of the world. Magnificent and impressive though it is, it seems increasingly partial and always to point beyond itself to a metaphysical and, in the only true sense, mystical view of the universe.[34]

The chief difficulty with a lot of us is the poverty-stricken view we have of nature and of our total environment. We have eyes and see not, ears and hear not. We look at the world and it is not wonderful. Reality has no greatness, makes no demands upon us. Oman[22] has argued that this is the malaise of this century, that much of our agnosticism is the denial of greatness around us, and failure to penetrate beyond the most superficial perception of our total environment. We have played too long on the surface and dulled our senses.

When I try to interpret what man is in all the richness of his aesthetic and moral and spiritual experience, and I cannot leave these out as they matter most, I find materialism lets me down. The only real entities in the materialistic or mechanistic view are bits of stuff; big bits like mountains, little bits like electrons. On the materialistic view, my most real experiences are brushed aside as illusion. However vague our language may be, mind and spiritual experience stand for something real for the Christian and for many who do not call themselves by that name. I interpret this as

c

meaning that there is, in man, a mental and spiritual as well as a physical component. The only doctrine of man that makes sense to me is the Christian concept of man as a dependent creature. He is not a closed system but an open system, dependent upon spiritual resources greater than himself. This is the *Milieu Divin* of Teilhard de Chardin. 'What is most divine in God is that, in an absolute sense, we are nothing apart from Him. . . . In action I adhere to the creative power of God; I coincide with it; I become not only its instrument but its living extension.'[35]

Man is open to spiritual resources that seem to flow as from a bottomless well. This is the view that man lives not by bread alone but by the values of existence. We know these in the depth of our experience. There is such a thing as human nature, which we all share. We experience an inner vacuum and emptiness until the resource which is beyond ourselves meets our need. That resource is always a quality or value. Our personalities are what they are by virtue of the values that have become concretely realized in us so that someone else will describe us as courageous, forgiving, patient and so on. It is putting it another way when Tillich says that a man is estranged until that which is of ultimate concern grasps him.[36] In this view the significance of man is not what he is, but what he can become and what he can reach after. The intellectual analysis of the experience of value and the interpretation of that experience first became real to me on reading Sorley's Gifford Lectures[37] and Hartmann's work on moral values.[38] Here were analyses of value experiences which gave a real content to the realm of values, and which lifted the interpretation of these experiences from the nature of epiphenomena to the nature of entities as real as the table on which I write.

Mind and Matter

For some time now, it has seemed inescapable to me that a universe in which life and mind and purpose and artistic and religious experiences are possible, requires a different sort of explanation from a universe in which these are not possibilities. 'That the world should give rise to minds which know the world involves a good deal concerning the nature of the world,' said William Temple.[11] Had we been observers from outer space of the evolution of the cosmos at the stage when all was no more organized than spinning nebulae, and had we then analysed the electrons and protons comprising those nebulae, we might have produced one sort of picture of the nature of that universe. But had we turned up at a later stage when sentient man was on the scene, would our interpretation of the nature of that universe have been the same? I think not. That man is possible in this world means that the world has properties that a world in which man is not possible does not have. Mind is not merely a product of nature's evolution, but one of the primary grounds of nature. I was introduced to this idea by my first professor of zoology, W. E. Agar, who wrote a little-known book on the subject.[39] Agar advised me to read all I could of A. N. Whitehead and Charles Hartshorne, which advice I gratefully took. Hartshorne later introduced me to this same thought in the distinguished evolutionary biologist Sewall Wright, who wrote: The emergence of even the simplest mind from no mind at all seems to me at least utterly incomprehensible. If, on the other hand, we turn the problem around and try to derive matter from mind, there is no such difficulty. We assume here that reality consists primarily of a multiplicity of minds. . . .'[40] But this is to anticipate the rest of the argument, so we must go back a step.

There are three possible ways in which mind and matter, or matter and experience, could be related. They can be stated thus:

Matter never experiences: this is the doctrine of mechanism, the corollary is that life is matter-like.

Matter always experiences: this is the doctrine of organic mechanism, the corollary is that matter is life-like.

Matter sometimes experiences (the matter in man): this is dualism (e.g. deism).

I have argued that the hallmark of man is that he is a sentient being, that there is a mental and spiritual side to his nature. He is a responsive creature. The only view that makes sense to me is the view which goes on from there to see the whole of nature in the perspective of our understanding of man. This is the second view listed above—matter always experiences. What I see clearly in man I see in principle as possible for all creation. This is to suppose that the universe is through and through, not bits of stuff, but that it has, in its ultimate nature, a physical aspect and a mental aspect, never separate but ever conjoined.

Matter and mind are not two things but two ways of looking at the one thing. One of the major philosophical problems of evolution disappears on this basis. It gets rid of the necessity of introducing mind into a previously mindless world when man appears on the scene. There is no direct evidence for asserting or denying this proposition. But if a more self-consistent and satisfying and coherent picture of the universe and its evolution can be constructed on the assumption that in its ultimate or its inner nature, the primary particles are, like ourselves, sentient, then physics can have nothing to say against it. Indeed some physicists, such as Weizsäcker[41] and Heisenberg,[16] are expressing just such a point of view.

Heisenberg says: 'It will probably be necessary for an understanding of life to go beyond quantum theory and to construct a new coherent set of concepts, to which physics and chemistry may belong as "limiting cases". . . . Concepts like perception, adaptation, affection will belong to it.' Heisenberg considers that the discoveries of modern physics mean that it is now impossible for physics to go back to the idea of a universe whose smallest parts exist as objects like billiard balls. The most important change brought about by the results of modern physics 'consists in the dissolution of this rigid frame of concepts of the nineteenth century'. He goes on to say that the elementary particle of modern physics is far more abstract than the atom of the Greeks and by this very property more consistent as a clue for the explanation of the behaviour of matter. Heisenberg now considers that the application of classical physics did not even fit into chemistry, 'therefore one is less inclined to assume that the concepts of physics, even those of quantum theory, can certainly be applied everywhere in biology or other sciences. . . . We will on the contrary try to keep the doors open for the entrance of new concepts even in those parts of science where the older concepts have been very useful to the understanding of phenomena.' At the biological level, new properties emerge which could never have been predicted from a study of atoms in the inorganic. Heisenberg leaves the door open for physics to receive new understanding from biology, though he is also well aware of the grave limitation in dealing with life, that our very methods of study tend to destroy what we are studying, that 'we murder to dissect'. The epigram of John Scott Haldane is coming true: 'If physics and biology one day meet, and one of the two is swallowed up, that one will not be biology.'[42]

The old dividing line between living and non-living has broken down; there is no sharp line of demarcation. You could choose to say, as some do, that life looks matter-like. Or you could argue, as I have done, that matter looks life-like; that it would be truer to say that the universe is a life than to say it is a mechanism. This idea, that organism rather than mechanism provides the clue to a philosophy of nature, is the point of view of A. N. Whitehead, and what he called the doctrine of 'organic mechanism'.[43] Man is not separate from nature, but a part of nature.

It is a paradox of this century that whereas physicists are moving more toward the non-mechanistic view of the universe, biologists by and large are still old-fashioned mechanists. They are distrustful of the philosophical ideas that have arisen, partly as a result of their own contributions. Some of their most vocal spokesmen are (as Greene[3] and Thorpe[34] have pointed out) almost schizophrenic in the language they use to describe life and evolution. They are very conscious of the stunning blow that Darwin gave to natural theology, and this has made them sceptical of any attempts to interpret nature on anything but mechanical lines. There are, of course, notable exceptions such as Thorpe,[34] Agar,[39] Sewall Wright,[40] Dobzhansky,[44] Dubos,[45] Chauvin[46] and Eccles.[47] But these are, amongst their colleagues, voices crying in a wilderness of traditional thinking.

The view I am commending is certainly no return to discredited natural theology, but a building on those elements that led to its downfall. It is the view that nature is, as Wordsworth said, 'something far more deeply interfused' than a closed system of mechanics. It is the idea expressed by another poet, Rabindranath Tagore: 'I believe in a spiritual world, not as something separated from this world, but as its real, innermost truth.' Our common mistake is 'to imagine the living sentient creature man as inhabiting an alien and indifferent physical universe by a sort of precarious squatter's right.'[48] We tend to think of inanimate and animate, the self-aware and the non-aware, as juxtaposed patches in a very patchy universe.

> *I, a stranger and afraid,*
> *In a world I never made.*[49]

So Thomas Henry Huxley asked, 'Is the universe friendly?' Is it a contrivance? Or is it more like a life? Is nature a dead stage on which man walks alone? These are questions asked by men in all ages. Science has made them more real than ever before. If there is to be an answer, science and theology must work together to discover it. At least one theologian agrees. Paul Tillich says:

> Of course, theology cannot rest on scientific theory. But it must relate its understanding of man to an understanding of universal nature, for man is a part of nature and statements about nature underlie every statement about him. . . . Even if the questions about the relation of man to nature and the universe could be avoided by theologians, they would still be asked by people of every place and time—often with existential urgency and out of cognitive honesty. And the lack of an answer can be a stumbling block for a man's whole religious life.[29]

The Universe Experiences God

If our clue to the nature of the universe is the sentient nature of man as the great experiencer, and if that leads us to suggest that all matter experiences, what is it that the universe including man experiences? My answer is God. This I shall develop in the next chapter. But something must be said now. This is a view of God very different from the one which much of orthodoxy gives. It is with a certain amount of fear and trembling that I introduce the word 'God' at this stage, as the concept of God in an experiencing universe is vastly different from the God of deism which is the picture so often conjured up in the modern mind when the word 'God' is mentioned. The meaningful starting point to the concept of God is the meaning of God in human experience. From there we can proceed at a later stage to find out if that meaning is relevant to the rest of the universe.

As Tillich says, God meets man in human experience as 'ultimate concern'. Every life has its concerns. Many of them are secondary, in the sense that they do not fill the vacuum of estranged human nature, the emptiness of life which is less than life could be. There is then an inner emptiness that expresses itself in depression, pursuit of endless pleasure, lust for power and eventually Freud's death instinct. None of these pursuits fulfils human life. They lead to deeper emptiness. That which fulfils human nature is what is meant by 'ultimate concern'. The 'ultimate concern' of human life for the Christian becomes concretely realized in Jesus Christ. He of all finite beings rejected all preliminary concerns, he crucified them for ultimate concern. Jesus crucified is the symbol of concrete realization of ultimate concern, which is always a quality of life, never a thing. It is always a value: for the woman in adultery—forgiveness; for the man in hypnotic paralysis by the pool—self confidence and the courage to be; for the young, rich man—sacrifice and service; for grief-stricken Mary and Martha—hope; for all—love. For these are what love is. There is only one response which is adequate to ultimate concern, it is 'with infinite passion'—which is Tillich's paraphrase of 'with all your heart and mind and soul and strength'.[50] There is hardly a more emphatic statement in all scripture than that. In a sense, you do not *have* ultimate concern, you are grasped by it. It is to be grasped by, and transformed by, the quality that made Jesus what he was, his humility, his pureness of heart, his forgiveness, his courage and sacrifice, his infinite concern for all men, from the rejected child to the thief on the cross. To experience that is to experience ultimate concern. The experience is personal.

God as ultimate concern is known in experience as two-fold—as sustainer and persuader. As sustainer or provider, it is the love that sustains my qualitative life. What I need in deepest need is a quality. I do not make it, I appropriate it. It is always accessible; the providence of God is not an assertion made at the beginning, but an experience. The symbols of God as sustainer are: 'bread of life', for man does not live by bread alone, 'water of life', which springs from a well of bottomless resource, 'very present help', 'refuge and strength', 'rod and staff'. As persuader, God is the love that lures to higher concern, the love that searches out like the shepherd, the pearl of great price, the treasure in the field, the light on the hill, the light that burns with consuming fire, the word that pierces, sharper than any two-edged sword. 'O Lord, thou hast searched me and known me.' 'Behold, I stand at the door and knock.' Many and varied are its expressions. The essence of Christian faith and life is the discovery at every point of life's need of a resource beyond ourselves that lifts and lures us and that transforms us into the likeness of itself. The resource is called God, who is known never as coercive power, but as persuasive love.

In confrontation with Christ, man becomes aware of his own incompleteness and of the estrangement of his own life from what he could be. The man who was estranged and separated from what he could be, becomes filled with a new ecstatic quality of life. His cup runs over. His is life abundant. When I refer to Jesus as 'Son of Man', it is because I see in that life a fulfilment of manhood. He was fully man because God was in him; not all of God, but that aspect of God that fulfils the possibilities of human life. He is not God masquerading as a man. If we think like that, it is because we have completely distorted the meaning of the symbols of Christian faith. Origen argued this out very clearly away back in the third century when he faced the charge by Celsus that Christians make a ridiculous claim that God left his heaven and descended on to the earth. 'God', he wrote, 'comes to us; yet he does not leave his home or desert his state. The result is not that one place is emptied of him while another is full, which did not before contain him.'

Christ is man, as we are man, yet filled with God. The life that was in him can be in us also, otherwise his call 'follow me' is a hollow call. The source of his life is the source of our lives whether or not we acknowledge that. How nobly Origen expressed this in his argument against

Celsus: 'From Jesus began a weaving together of the divine and human nature in order that human nature, through fellowship with what is more divine, might become divine, not only in Jesus but also in all those who, besides believing in Jesus, take up the life which he taught; the life which leads everyone who lives according to the precepts of Jesus to friendship with God and fellowship with him.' We follow Jesus because we see in him the way. The truth about human life, the meaning for human life, cannot be found in anything less than personal. So Jesus says, 'I am the truth', not 'I teach the truth'. The truth about life is not a theory about life, but a life.

What I have said is brief and therefore inadequate. It may suffice to underline one point, that in the Christian view, the purpose of human life is to attain the fulness of the stature of man, which is to be Christ-like. From the Godward view, it is the concrete realization of divine possibilities in human life, the making real of God in the world.

This idea of God's purpose in human life is very different from the concept of God as determining in every detail the pathway and destiny of every individual, as though the details of our lives are mapped out on a divine chart, and our job is to discover the map. The providence of God is not the protection he gives us on life's path from accidents, suffering, disease and death. He does not. The providence of God is that there is no situation in which a man may find himself which puts him beyond the resource that can meet his deepest needs. And these are never things but always values. 'There is nothing love cannot face; there is no limit to its faith.' 'I am convinced that there is nothing in death or life, in the realm of spirits or superhuman powers, in the world as it is or the world as it shall be, in the forces of the universe, in heights or depths—nothing in all creation that can separate us from the love of God.' So wrote Paul (I Cor. 13.7; Rom. 8.38-9, NEB). In the depths of man's need, his need is for 'courage to be', hope, forgiveness. He is never cut off from the source of these resources, unless he cuts himself off. He is free to choose.

The outreach of God in our valuational experience is the meaning of God as the source of love. We should see how vastly different this view is from deism which puts the emphasis on God as power. He is power to do anything at all, power to turn St Paul's Cathedral into the Taj Mahal; but he restrains himself. It presents the absurdity of the picture of a God who calculates whether he should do what he could do, and mostly decides not to. By demolishing this picture, the atheists and agnostics think they have demolished Christianity.[51] They have, instead, done the Christian religion a service. Traditional Christianity of the West is deeply infected with the power concept of God. It does not take love seriously. As Raven once said, 'it has never been adequately Christianized'.[52] But God does not compete with the earthquake. Oman made a moving plea to challenge the idea of God's activity as 'the might of omnipotence directed in an unswerving line by omniscience'.[53] Raven makes a similar appeal to love as against power. Here is his paraphrase of the conclusion of the evolution of Paul's thought from God as power to God as love. Speaking to the Corinthians, Paul says:

> The Jews seek after miracles, they are beset with an idea of God as a God of power, a Sultan, a miracle worker. The Greeks are crazy for wisdom, they think of God in terms of the supreme Philosopher, the supreme Mathematician, the supreme Engineer. But we are not satisfied with a picture of God in terms either of power or wisdom. We see God in terms of a man on a cross, of the love that suffers, and suffering redeems. We see God not in terms of a Sultan, nor an Engineer, neither of Judge nor of Designer. We see God in terms of our Father.[52]

Is God then powerless? No—there is a power in love! There is power in persuasive love that is greater than all other sorts of power. There is no need for any other sort of power. It is because we are unconvinced of the power of persuasive love that we want to invest God with dictatorial coercive power.

The principle of persuasive love as the divine influence implies that man is free to choose. 'Here I stand knocking at the door; if anyone hears my voice and opens the door, I will come in . . .' (Rev. 3.20). That is the symbol both of divine love and of man's freedom. If man be free, then evil is possible. If there were no freedom, there would be no virtue. Man would be an automaton and all would be out of his hands. For God to control man would be to destroy man; we are responsible creatures. There is no possibility of purpose in human life if man has no purposes to choose from. The principle of divine love is consistent with the possibility of evil and this includes moral evil and what is sometimes called the evil of nature. This is a problem to be considered when we discuss God and the world, but it is necessary at this stage to anticipate one aspect of what must be developed later. In a universe under the principle of divine love where freedom operates, 'accidents' will happen. God does not guarantee the 'safety' of any creature in this universe. Love never does. Mature religion can accept this. In Ecclesiastes 9.11 we read: 'I returned, and saw under the sun, that the race is not to the swift, nor the battle to the strong, neither yet bread to the wise, nor yet riches to men of understanding, nor yet favour to men of skill; but time and chance happeneth to them all.'

I doubt if any philosopher has more consistently built the fact of chance into his philosophical scheme than Hartshorne.[54, 55] For him, chance is a necessary aspect of a purposive universe. He writes:

> The alternative, chance *or* providence, is invalid. . . .
> Chance is just as real as some of the atheists have been telling us during the centuries. But chance is within limits . . .

chance not limited at all is sheer chaos. . . . The reality of chance is the very thing that makes providence significant, as I believe any rigorous development of the cosmological argument will show. As with so many traditional issues, such as that between absolutism and relativism, so with this one between blind chance and teleology or providence, the solution is, *both*—though not in respect to the same aspect of existence. And no longer do we face the cruel alternative: either no divine control or the deliberate divine contriving of all our woes. The detail of events—and our sufferings are among the details—are not contrived, or planned, or divinely decreed. They just happen—period. What is decreed is that it shall be possible for them to happen, but also possible for other, and partly better, things to happen.[54]

Christ the 'Within' of All Things

If human life is to be interpreted in relation to a God of persuasive love rather than coercive power, then it is reasonable to investigate the possibility that this is a symbol of the relationship of God to the universe. This we must pursue later. It will involve the proposition that if Christ is the key to the meaning of human life, if he is the light that lightens every man that comes into the world, then he will be (symbolically) the light that falls upon the world into which every man comes. Sittler has pointed out that this is a radical proposition for the Western world.[55] The idea of interpreting the whole of nature in the light of the nature of man has not had a very popular career in the Western world, though Sittler remarks that the contrary is true of Eastern Christendom, as for example in the thought of Irenaeus. 'The rood-screen in the church has become a symbol of man's devout but frightened thought permitting to fall asunder what God joined together.'[56] Western Christendom has tended to claim that man is the only possible avenue of incarnation. But the world is sustained by incarnation of God in every entity and every creative advance.

'The world lives', says Whitehead, 'by its incarnation of God in itself.'[57] This is to use the word 'incarnation' in a non-literal sense, to include all manifestations of God in the universe. This is quite a legitimate meaning of the word in addition to its narrower meaning of the manifestation of God in a particular human life. Writing in the third century, Origen (*De Principiis*) reminds us: 'The incarnation is not a sudden intervention of a God hitherto negligent, like Zeus awakening from sleep. God had always been working for the good of the human race. For nothing good has happened to men except by the indwelling of the Divine Logos. . . .' Having strayed far from the reasonable path that Origen set out, Christians now adhere to an incarnation limited in both time and space. This incarnation is indeed limited when compared with the doctrine which we find in Psalm 24: ('The earth is the Lord's and the fulness thereof, the world, and they that dwell therein'); or in the opening of the Fourth Gospel, or in the words of John 5.17 ('My father has never yet ceased his work, and I am working too'); or in Paul's letter to the Colossians with its theme of Christ and 'all things', the theme which sums up a reasoned faith that can make sense of science as of life.

'He is the image of the invisible God' (Col. 1.15). Paul is saying that Jesus is the manifestation of the nature of God. The purpose of man is none other than to make the nature of God real in the world. Look here at Jesus, he says, he shows you not only what God is, but also what man is meant to be. Here in fulfilled manhood is the manifestation of God. The outer aspect is the man, but he is only understood in terms of the inner aspect of fulfilled manhood, and that is God manifested in him.

'His is the primacy over all created things' (Col. 1.15). Paul is not speaking about priority in time, but priority in importance. Barclay remarks that primacy or firstborn 'is not used in a time sense at all but in the sense of special honour'.[58] In all creation, there is nothing bigger, nothing higher, nothing more fully manifesting the nature of God than Jesus Christ. If you do not see that, he is saying, you miss the whole point of the universe. This is where you start in your understanding of all creation.

'In him everything in heaven and earth was created' (Col. 1.16). He is, says Paul, not only our revelation of the 'within' of man, but the 'within' of all things. What you see in him I now show you in all things! Here is the 'wisdom' of God you have been looking for, the *logos* or Word of God, the manifestation or whatever you may want to call it. In Christ that *logos*, that 'within' of things, is plain for all to see. Here we see the same principle by which 'all things cohere' (Col. 1.17).

Paul was not writing all this in a vacuum, but to a church at Colossae which had evidently been much influenced by Gnostic thinking. The Gnostics saw the world as evil, created by an evil God. They conceived of Jesus as a sort of divine ghost whose feet could not even leave footprints on the evil sand of the world. Nature to the Gnostics was evil. We no longer think like that. Instead, we just think of nature as a mechanism, purposeless mechanism grinding its way to inevitable annihilation! To us, Paul says what he said to Colossae: 'Look here to the person of Christ and find the clue, not only to your own existence, but to all existence. You will then see all existence in a new light.'

Some claim that science has to do with the question 'what', and religion with the question 'why'. But it is better to say that although science may restrict itself to what is, religion should be concerned as much with the nature of nature as with purpose in nature. Indeed, the answer to 'why' will determine the answer to 'what it is'. So John Macmurray says: 'Religion cannot escape from the need to express the relation of the world to God, and of man to the world, and in both cases a conception of the actual nature of the world is indispensable. So we must agree that so far as religion is concerned with a conception of the character and structure of the actual world, it is identical in principle with science.'[59]

The *purpose* of nature and the *nature* of nature are what the concept 'creation' is all about. It is to see the universe in a certain way, with a certain sort of unity. If we cut nature up into sections, one labelled 'science' and another labelled 'religion', we should remember that it is we who are doing the cutting up. The robe of nature is a seamless one. When you do cut it up, you can never put it together again. There is no part of the world which is secular and another sacred. We have this narrow view, says Tillich, because of the 'tragic estrangement of man's spiritual life from its own ground and depth'. Tillich follows this remark with the reminder that the visionary who wrote the last book of the Bible tells us there will be no temple in the heavenly Jerusalem. 'There will be no secular realm, and for this very reason there will be no religious realm.'[60]

4

CREATION AND THE BIBLE

*The word creation is one of the great symbol-words
describing the relation of God to the Universe.*
Paul Tillich, *Systematic Theology*, vol. III.

The Symbol of Creation

WHAT does the word 'creation' convey to modern minds?
To many it is an idea now discredited by science—though
once widely believed—and having to do with how things
began. They think of it as a series of fabulous fiats by God
in the distant past whereby in a frenzy of activity, he
brought forth the universe from nothing. This was widely
believed in the seventeenth, eighteenth and nineteenth centuries. It is still an article of belief of some Christian sects
to this day. And that is a reason why others reject the Christian faith. In quite another sense some cosmologists and
physicists talk about 'continuous creation' as something
that is going on now in the expanding physical universe. In
some form or other the concept of creation has entered into
the credal statements of Christians, though from the rela-
tive silence of present-day theologians on the subject, one
might be excused for supposing that they no longer regard
it as very important. Something has happened to this symbol. To many it has come to mean either something irrelevant or something ridiculous. And yet, creation is a symbol
of the central theme of the Judaeo-Christian faith. I am
using the word 'symbol' here in the meaning of picture or
analogy. As Tillich reminds us in the quotation which heads
this chapter, the word 'creation' stands for a tremendous
idea about the relation of God to the universe. If what is

central is now neglected or turned into a laughing stock, then it is Christians who are largely to blame. When they have taken the symbols of the Christian faith literally, they have made them ridiculous. This is what has largely happened to the symbol of creation. No reconciliation is possible between the literalism of the 'biblicist' or fundamentalist concept of creation and the modern world view of science. It is a tragedy that failure to look beyond the words to the meaning they convey has, for many, put an impassable barrier between religion and science. In this chapter, I want to do little more than clear a way for a rediscovery of a depth of meaning to the symbol of creation.

The meaning behind the symbol of creation is profoundly relevant to the central argument of the earlier chapters. I have argued there that the concept of the 'billiard ball' universe, that is a universe as a contrivance and no more, was totally inadequate. The foundations of the self-creating, self-sustaining contrivance have been severely shaken. The alternative proposition I have proposed is that the universe has both an outer mechanical aspect and an inner aspect which is akin to mind. This involves the idea that man and all entities are in some sense sentient, all are 'experiencers', although in different degree. All are dependent systems. All are open and not closed systems.

But what does the universe experience? What is it sensitive to? The meaning of 'creation' is the answer that *the universe experiences God*. To make any sense of this proposition we begin with man the experiencer. It makes sense of man to see him as dependent upon God for his qualitative life, the life of mind and spirit. The question we are then led on to is whether the whole universe is, in some analogous way, dependent upon God for its being? This would of course have to include man in both his physical being as well as his qualitative being. The concept of creation is that this is the nature of the universe and all that is in it. The universe and all that is in it can only be understood in relation to God. If we reject the concept of the universe as contrivance and no more, then this seems to me the one valid alternative open to us. It all depends, of course, upon what we mean by 'God'.

Creation in the Bible

To some modern minds an appeal to a biblical concept implies a return to the Sunday-school picture-book concept of God. That we reject. To others it implies that we are invited to indulge in some form of mental gymnastics which will put together all ideas of God in the Bible, from that of the tribal God of vengeance to the loving father, into one coherent concept. That too we reject. Not all concepts of God in the Bible are worthy. Some are quite pre-Christian, glorifying power and hatred. But there are others. There is a high theme about God which begins at the beginning and is never completely lost right to the end, though it gets somewhat submerged at times. I am not saying that because it is in the Bible it is true. What I am saying is that the hundreds of years of concern about God and the universe that the Bible portrays, have yielded an insight that is amazingly relevant to our search today. There are other sources that are also extremely relevant and we shall most certainly need to draw upon this wisdom as well.

The meaning of God *in human life* as portrayed in the Bible is a relevant point of departure for a consideration of the meaning of God in the universe at large. This is, in fact, the order of development of the idea of God in Judaeo-Christian thinking. It is a serious mistake to interpret the Genesis story as the foundation for all subsequent thought about creation. On the contrary, literary analysis suggests that the Genesis stories came rather late in the history of development of the Old Testament.[1] The religious Hebrew mind was almost entirely concerned with questions of meaning and purpose in human life and the life of the nation. Its primary insight was the conception of God as active in human life and the conception of man as dependent upon God. From his conception of God's activity in human life, the Hebrew was led on by analogy to a conception of divine activity in the non-human part of existence. As Bultmann says: 'Man was not interpreted in the light of the world but the world in the light of man.'[2] Religious consciousness started from self-valuation, but broadened into the concept of the world. That was the sequence of Hebrew thought about God, not only in Genesis, but also in the creation psalms (Psalms 8; 19; 104; 148), in the tenth chapter of Jeremiah, in the creation passages in the book of Job (38-41), and in the famous fortieth chapter of Isaiah. The word the Hebrews used for God's activity, be it in man or in the world, was 'create'. 'Create' is divine activity. The same idea is expressed by Wren-Lewis: 'The true origin of the idea of a Creator God arises . . . not from any sort of argument about design in nature, indeed not from any speculative argument at all, but from the immediate experience of a creative Power in personal life, in the social relations of men with each other.'[3]

Creation then has not to do primarily with *origins*. It has primarily to do with *dependence*, man's dependence upon God's activity and subsequently by analogy the dependence of all creation upon God's activity. It is not a story which begins 'once upon a time'. It has not to do with how things began but how they are; what they are in their inner nature. And their nature is interpreted in terms of dependence upon God. We might use the word 'sustain' as almost synonymous with 'create'. Some theologians use the more technical phrase 'ground of being' to describe God's sustaining relation to all creation. It is the idea that nothing that is or has ever been, is without that dependence. It is the idea that you cannot think of God as something in addition to, or beside, the universe. The universe is dependent in the sense that if God at this moment ceased to be, the universe would collapse. Job expressed this concept when he said:

'If he (God) gathers unto himself his spirit and his breath; all flesh shall perish together, and man shall turn again unto dust' (34.14). This is not an identification of God with the world, which is pantheism. God is not *identified with*, but he is *involved* in, all that is.

There is, then, no real distinction between an original creation and continuing creation. Bultmann says that the real purpose of the creation story is to indicate what God is doing *all the time*.[2] The same view was expressed by William Temple in *Nature, Man and God*: 'It is the claim that Spirit is not only a source of initiation, but is the only source of the whole world-process. All the more developed religions, which do not deny the reality of matter, have advanced this claim. It is the doctrine of creation.' And he goes on to say that it is of no direct importance to religion to assert a date for the act of creation, or even to assert that it is an act having any date at all; it may be a never-beginning and never-ending activity. Westermann says there is no passage in the Bible which was written to inform the present generation, or for that matter any generation, about the procedure or the act or the acts of creation.[4] These theologians maintain that it is a false interpretation of the Bible to suppose that creation has to do with how things began. For that matter, there may not have been a beginning.

'Creation' Today

How did the emphasis of creation become so tragically misplaced in traditional Christian thought? There are at least two reasons which I shall consider briefly. One has to do with the failure to understand the meaning of myth. The second has to do with the traditional doctrine known as *creatio ex nihilo*. I am not an authority on either of these matters, but there are many clues to the first and a few to the second which are quite accessible these days to anyone who wants to pursue them in the writings of Barth,[5] Bultmann,[2] Tillich,[6] and other theologians such as Gilkey[7] and most recently Evans.[8] There are right questions and wrong questions to ask about anything. When a person asks the wrong question you can give no answer. When a person asks about the Genesis stories, 'Did it really happen that way?' there can be no answer, for we cannot hear what the writers are saying. We can only be utterly confused. But if a person asks, 'What does it mean today?' we can respond.

There is in Genesis not one story, but two. Man is created in Gen. 1.27, and created all over again in a different sequence in Gen. 2.7. The first account moves from the creation of light, the world and living creatures to man. The second begins with man, then a rather restricted list of living creatures and leads up to the creation of woman. This is confusion to the literalist, but not to those who understand these stories as biblical 'myths', or as Karl Barth prefers to call them 'sagas'. The nature of 'myths', be they in the Bible or in the writings of other religions, is that they do not mean what they literally say. They have to be interpreted. The process of interpretation is sometimes called 'demythologization'. This is not directed against the use of myths, as Tillich points out, but is directed against 'the supranaturalistic method which takes these images literally'. There is nothing new about this approach. It was accepted by early fathers of the Christian Church. In the third century, Origen explicitly rejects a literal interpretation of Genesis 1. 'What man of intelligence', he asks, 'will believe that the first, and second, and third day, and evening and morning existed without the sun and moon and stars?' Nor did he regard Adam as a historical personage, but as a symbol of humanity.[9] But what Origen could see 1,700 years ago is still not seen by many people who call themselves Christian today! Modern biblical scholarship suggests that the authors of Genesis 1 themselves had no intention of writing a 'historical' narrative. The form of the whole account suggests that it is a deliberately symbolic account of the divine activity within and underlying all nature.

A number of myths may say different things but point to the one meaning. Indeed, the point of the story is more likely to get across if it is embodied in not one, but a number of stories. So it is common to all systems of communication by myth that all important stories recur in several different versions. What the literalist finds as a stumbling-block and a defect is to the demythologizer an essential part of this mode of communication. This ancient and esoteric mode of communication has a modern ring about it when we see it in the light of 'information theory'. Leach has made a most interesting analysis of some of the biblical myths in these terms.[10] In all forms of transfer of information, the message is coded. In this form, it is transmitted but against a background of a certain amount of 'noise' or interference. The code may be morse-code, or any number of different sorts of signal. It is received with a certain amount of noise, in addition to the original signal transmitted. Our problem is to translate the signal and reduce the noise. Often the noise gets in the way of the signal and the signal then means different things to different receivers. The whole of Christendom shares in a single corpus of 'myths', some borrowed from other religions, but each sect tends to convince itself that it alone possesses the secret of the message. There is, in principle, a more objective approach to the interpretation of myth, which Leach suggests. It is the analysis of the myth into its components (for myths have an identifiable structure) which can then be arranged or 'programmed' for a computer. The resulting analysis tends to clarify any consistent message more objectively than might otherwise be possible. The task is a very big one and, as yet, not a great deal has been done. In the meantime, we can get some measure of understanding by looking for the depth of meaning in the myth rather than reading it as a literal story, which it is not.

This approach to sacred writings is, of course, an essential in reading documents of historic events as it is in reading 'myths'. We read, for example, in II Kings 20.35: 'And it came to pass that night that the angel of the Lord went forth and smote in the camp of the Assyrians an hundred and four score and five thousand; and when the men arose early in the morning, behold, they were all dead corpses.' The angel of the Lord was probably a plague of field mice. The ecologist Charles Elton has drawn attention to the statement by the historian Herodotus in the fifth century BC, concerning this same event. 'The disaster was brought about by field mice, which, pouring in upon the soldiers, devoured their quivers, bow-strings and the handles of their shields so that the next day when they fled bereft of their arrows they were slain.' The event was commemorated by a statue of the Egyptian king Séthon in the temple of Vulcan, the king holding a mouse in his hand. So even the zoologist may make his contribution to the interpretation of ancient writings![11]

A second aspect of misplaced emphasis in the doctrine of creation in traditional Christianity was the development of the doctrine that became known as *creatio ex nihilo*. This says that creation is the making by God of something out of nothing. The doctrine arose, as most doctrines did, as a defence against the ideas of certain Greeks which Christians regarded as pagan. These were the Gnostics who taught that the world and God had always existed together, that the world was bad and was created by a bad God. Pelikan considers that the doctrine *creatio ex nihilo* was first explicitly stated by Theophilus of Antioch, one of the very early Greek 'apologists' for Christianity. Later it was elaborated by Tertullian. The Gnostics whom Tertullian opposed said that the bad God was the God of the Old Testament. Tertullian set out to convince Christians that the same God who redeems man also made the world; there was no opposition party to God in creation. His way of denying the anti-God principle of the Gnostics was to assert that God made the world out of nothing. This interpretation of the doctrine of creation became an emphasis from that point onwards. It is strongly asserted by Aquinas and by the Protestant reformers, though there is nothing particularly biblical about 'creation out of nothing'. Pelikan says that where the technical term 'create' is used in the Bible, the issue of *creatio ex nihilo* is not raised.[12]

This particular emphasis of the concept of creation, which arose as a polemic, had very unhappy consequences with the rise of science. It became an obvious target for the darts of science that fell thick and fast from the seventeenth century onwards. Just when it was needed most, the original emphasis of creation as God's sustaining and continuous activity was buried in the background. When science began to say something about the universe, Christians could only produce a concept of God as creating things out of nothing by a series of dramatic fiats at the beginning of time.

There is no literal sense in which the idea of creation out of nothing has meaning. Whitehead has said, 'You cannot approach nothing; for there is nothing to approach'.[13] Moreover, it is a concept that has not led to a single philosophical idea of any importance. And as far as theology is concerned, it makes no difference whether or not the universe did have a beginning (see also Mascall[14]). The doctrine seems to have outlived the usefulness it had when formulated, though Tillich[6] sees in it still a twofold symbol for Christians. It points, he says, to the idea that evil is not the essential nature of things, and secondly that there is an element of what he calls 'non-being' in every creature. Be that as it may, this does seem to be a roundabout way of expressing such ideas now.

Positively and permanently, the doctrine of creation affirms that man and the world reveal the nature of the divine activity which is their ground of being. We need to regrasp within the context of the modern world what the

Church in former times grasped firmly, though it had a simpler world with which to be concerned. Who can gaze upon the mosaics of the great Basilica of St Apollinare in Classe on the outskirts of Ravenna without an overwhelming sense that the central figure of Christ on the cross in the apse is one with the flowers and birds, the grassy slopes and the lambs, in fact the whole world of real things? Here is a 'pan-sacramentalism' which Eastern Christendom never completely lost. At a later date, the great medieval cathedrals of Europe expressed the same conception of God in all things with their representations in stone of animals and plants and the tools of the craftsman. This was all part of the sacramental work of the cathedral. The emptiness of the Puritan churches of New England symbolizes the very opposite—the loss of any high evaluation of the world and nature and the sharp division between the sacred and the secular.

The doctrine of creation stands for the sacredness of all things. If we could recapture its inner meaning, the effect could be profound. A world bent on obliterating and exploiting nature for its pleasures might come again to a sense of deep concern wherever the opposite influence of destruction and devaluation holds sway.

> *'Twould ring the bells of Heaven*
> *The wildest peal for years,*
> *If Parson lost his senses*
> *And people came to theirs,*
> *And he and they together*
> *Knelt down with angry prayers*
> *For tamed and shabby tigers*
> *And dancing dogs and bears,*
> *And wretched, blind pit ponies,*
> *And little hunted hares.*[15]

5

THE MEANING OF CREATION

*The starting point for natural theology is not an argu-
ment but sharpened awareness. For the moment it is
better for us that the arguments have fallen to pieces.*
Paul Tillich, *Systematic Theology*, vol. III.

*It is impossible to mediate on time and the mystery of
the creative passage of nature without an overwhelming
emotion at the limitations of human intelligence.*
A. N. Whitehead, *The Concept of Nature.*[1]

God in the Universe

W E are now ready to look more analytically at the nature
of God's creative activity in the universe. I have contrasted
two ways of looking at the universe, as mechanical contrivance on the one hand, or as an experiencing universe on
the other. These two views provide two ways of looking at
what happened in cosmic evolution. In the mechanical
view, the history of nature is a rearrangement of increasingly complex patterns of the physicist's fundamental particles starting with the electron and leading to man. Qualities such as mind, which appear to be real in man, are not
real at all. What are real are the fundamental particles as
described by the physicist. Nothing evolves as there is
nothing to evolve in this system. All that can happen is a
rearrangement. In the other view, the history of nature is a
history of a progressive unfolding or revealing of what is
potentially possible in the universe. The history of nature is
a history of the actualization of possibilities. It is the making
real of the possibilities of God in the concrete world. It is
the progressive removal of restraints on matter. It is the

increase in sensitivity of the creation, in awareness and perception of the total environment which includes God. It is the enrichment of God's experience as the world reacts on God.

This is at base the Christian concept of creation in a modern dress. It is not one massive monolithic structure of thought, but a great web of thought that has strands of many colours, woven into a pattern of the unity of nature, man and God. There are no sharp breaks in the pattern and no end to the picture that is woven. It stretches beyond to yet undiscovered reaches of thought. It is an adventure of ideas without bounds, but with a sense of a firm foundation. It provides no guarantee of its veracity. It is a faith in the coherence and order of nature. It is an adventure of the imagination which joins with the great imaginative thoughts of all ages. Nor should we be afraid of that. Are life and religion and science concerned only with what can be proven once and for all without a shadow of a doubt? Neither scientists nor men of faith in other fields speak of life and thought in such terms today. The great ideas of the past on which so much of modern civilization depends, including the key ideas of modern science, were wrought in the imagination of men who battled in thought with what at first they only dimly saw, though firmly felt.[2] This, I believe, is also the nature of reasoned Christian faith. It is not a belief in a static formulation, but a sense of being grasped by something of tremendous importance that calls forth from a man all his powers of imaginative thought and of feeling and of action. The poet William Blake said it thus in his essay *To the Christians*:

> I know of no other Christianity and of no other Gospel than the liberty both of body and mind to exercise the divine arts of imagination—imagination, the real and eternal world of which this vegetable universe is but a faint shadow. . . . The Apostles knew of no other Gospel. What were all their spiritual gifts? What is the divine spirit? Is the Holy Ghost

any other than an intellectual fountain? What is the harvest
of the Gospel and its labourers? What is that talent which it
is a curse to hide? What are the treasures of heaven that we
are to lay up for ourselves?

Are not they all, Blake asks, gifts of the spirit of God which
a man receives in his mind as mental and spiritual gifts?
They are the rewards of the adventures of life and thought.

What is to follow goes beyond the facts, to speculate
about a framework within which the facts may be put and
which, to some of us at least, helps to make sense of the
facts. The discussion proceeds under six headings. The
headings are six affirmations about the meaning of creation.
No one has proved even a single one of them to be facts
about which we can be certain, without a shadow of a
doubt. There are some facts of which I can be certain. I
have no doubt that the time the pendulum takes to complete
its sway is the same, whether the amplitude of the sway be
large or small. That is a fact. I can measure it for myself and
be sure. But it is childish in the extreme to suppose that the
only knowledge we can handle has to be of that cut and
dried nature. As Whitehead has said, 'The task of reason is
to fathom depths of the many-sidedness of things. We must
not expect simple answers to far-reaching questions. However far our gaze penetrates, there are always heights
beyond that block our vision.'[3]

I have tried to write what follows in that spirit and with a
minimum of hedging. That I trust will help to highlight the
issues. It is done with a risk of appearing more dogmatic
than I wish to be, but the six propositions are not a series of
dogmatic assertions. They are a set of propositions for the
reader's serious consideration.

1. *Creation is the concrete realization of what is potentially
    possible in the universe.*

When there was no life on earth, there was the possibility
of life. With first-life there was the possibility of man. We

could imagine that there might be other sorts of universes in which these were not possibilities. The nature of our universe is such that these were potentialities or possibilities of the chaos. Thomas Henry Huxley appreciated this almost a hundred years ago. He regarded the idea of potentiality existing in the chaos before the universe evolved, as quite basic to Darwinian evolution. He even went so far as to call this a 'new teleology' to replace the 'old teleology' of William Paley.[4] I believe he was right.

The order of nature only makes sense against the background of the possibility of disorder or chaos. Order and disorder go together. It is from disorder or a less ordered state that order comes. I can recall Professor Hartshorne once speaking of order as ameliorated disorder, anarchy tamed! Tillich speaks of 'creation and chaos' as belonging to each other.[5] Berdyaev speaks of creation from a chaos 'which is alive and kicking with all sorts of possibilities'.[6] The ordering of the universe is the problem of creation. But there could be no order unless the potentiality for order existed even in the primal chaos.

Creation is the concrete realization of what is possible, so that out of chaos comes order. The possibilities are provided by God. In a sense this can be considered to define at least one aspect of God's nature. The realm of potentiality is what Whitehead has called 'the primordial nature of God'.[3] It is the aspect of God expressed in another image by Berdyaev[6] when he says that God created the world through imagination. In his primordial nature God lures the world to completeness, and provides it with its 'experience'. This is to sustain the world. In his primordial nature God is 'the absolute wealth of potentiality' of the universe. God confronts the world in his primordial nature which is the lure of unrealized possibility. The world experiences God as the world is created. So do men. 'The purpose of God is the attainment of value in the temporal world,' says Whitehead.[3] We are dependent and so is the electron. This brings

mind and perception in some germ of a sense right down to
the ultimate particles of the physicist. It is the proposition
that there is no such thing as mere matter, that is, matter
without experience. The electron is not feelingless mechanism. At its heart it is feeling. Reality is an 'ocean of feelings'. Reality is not stuff, reality is 'process'. And so Hartshorne asks, 'What scientist as such stands up to be counted
on the question, where is the lower limit of feeling in the
plant–animal series, or even is willing to say there is or can
be a lower limit?'[9] Apart from experience, there is 'nothing,
nothing, nothing, bare nothingness!'[3] We 'thingify' the electron and all other 'organisms' because we see them as static
mechanisms, and not as perceiving entities.

This is *not* to assert that such entities are conscious. The
word 'feeling' is used as an analogy to conscious feeling but
not to mean 'conscious feeling'. If we were really to know
what an electron was, we would have to be an electron, to
feel what it would be from within, but that we cannot do
any more than we can know what it is to be a tiger. We only
know that which we possess, we know then from within in
awareness. We can only know the electron 'imaginatively'
from that point of view. But presumably God knows what it
is to be an electron. That may be an experience for him. In
some sense he possesses it. He is part of its being, the part
that is experienced or 'felt' by the mind aspect of the electron. And so with each successive level of organization of
the material world. These ideas are strange to many ears, for,
as Tillich has said, 'a theology of the inorganic is lacking'.[10]

The lure of God in the creation is analogous to the lure
of purpose in our conscious lives. A conscious purpose is a
real cause in determining the course our lives take. But the
details of that course depend upon many things, some
mechanical, some accidental and quite unpredictable. This
was the famous distinction between 'final' and 'mechanical'
causes made by Socrates in prison, as reported in the
Phaedo. The cause of his being imprisoned was that he had

chosen to espouse certain ideals; the Athenians had con-
demned him in consequence, and he had chosen not to run
away. But he speaks too of the mechanical causes involved
in his being there, such as the movement of his bones and
muscles. Some would argue that these were the causes of
his actions. 'But if any one should say that without possess-
ing such things as bones and sinews, and whatever else I
have, I could not do what I pleased, he would speak the
truth; but to say that I do as I do through them, and that I
act thus by intelligence, and not from choice of what is best,
would be a great and extreme disregard of reason.' Baillie
has commented on this passage, that the whole history of
Western thought can be conceived as the story of how
various thinkers have dealt with this issue, first clearly set
before them by Socrates.[11]

I have been proposing the view that the activity of God
in the world has to do not with 'mechanical causes', but
with 'final causes'. Final causes are of the nature of purposes and values. God's purposes embody what is potentially possible for the world. They are not achieved by
mechanical intervention, but by the persuasive lure of value
and purpose. God, in this view, sets the limits to what can
be achieved. His is not the role of determining the mechanical details. There is no clash with science in this point of
view. God is not invoked to account for this or that chemical reaction or this or that mutation. God is not every
cause. Theology in the past has too often assigned mechanical causation to God with the inevitable consequence of a
head-on collision with science. The task of the philosopher
of religion is to assign specific causes to God's activity.
These, I am contending, are of the nature of final causes.

To be more specific than that would be to embark upon a
metaphysical adventure beyond the scope of this book. It is
being done by philosophers competent to handle such difficult issues. Probably no bolder attempt has ever been made
than Whitehead's philosophy of organic mechanism,[3] even

though Thomas Aquinas and others grappled profoundly with the problem on their pre-scientific medieval premises. Much thinking has yet to be done. Certainly no one has said the last word that can be said. I interpret this as being the attitude of the theologian Williams when he writes: 'Most of modern theology seems to agree that Calvin's assignment of efficient causality to God in every detail of existence is impossible. But we shall have to interpret that aspect of the total religious problem which Calvin saw clearly, the priority, the initiative, and the efficacy of divine "power".'[12] I would ask, Does not *persuasive love* provide all the initiative and 'power' that is necessary? Hartshorne and Reese, commenting on Whitehead, make no qualifications:

> There is no 'power' anywhere on earth or in heaven, except the direct and indirect workings of attractiveness ('persuasion'). We have power over other men's minds through the value they find in our thoughts and feelings; we have power over our bodies because the sentient units composing them derive such inspiration as their lowly natures can receive from these same thoughts and feelings; and through controlling our own bodies we can indirectly influence other men's bodies and minds. But the direct influence of God is analogous only to the direct power of thought over thought, and of feeling over feeling, and this is the power of inspiration or suggestion. It could not possibly suppress all freedom in the recipient, since a minimum of response on his part is presupposed.[13]

The Christian's symbol of God as persuasive love is the humility of the cross. In this view, persuasive love is the 'solitary route to redemption'. None other is needed. But as Whitehead has said: 'The brief Galilean vision of humility flickered throughout the ages, uncertainly. . . . The Church gave unto God the attributes which belonged exclusively to Caesar.' The original Galilean ministry 'dwells upon the tender elements in the world, which slowly and in quietness operate by love'.[3]

D

If all God's activity is of the nature of persuasive love, there must be room in the universe for spontaneity of response, a degree of self-determination on the part of the creature, and room for the accidental and unpredictable. It was the fatal error of deism to suppose that the one place where God did operate was in the unpredictable, the calamitous and the inexplicable. Darwin's dilemma was his tendency to suppose that if there were a God, he must be directly responsible for everything to the minutest detail. But God is not every cause. The parable of the sower makes this point. God sows only the 'good' seed (Mark 4.1, 14-20). We are determined not only by the good seed. There are weeds that come up and tend to choke the growth from the good seed, there is stony soil that is unreceptive to the good seed, there is scorching sun that burns the tender growth, and so on.

The view of God as causal purpose but not all causes is so important that, for fear of misunderstanding, I shall illustrate the idea further with two 'parables of light'.

Hocking[14] has suggested that we might think of God's role in the world as similar to the light that projects the motion picture on the screen. The light does not interfere with the activity of the figures and objects on the screen. It sustains the whole panorama of events. If it ceases all activity ceases and there are no players to act. They all depend upon it and it is not one of them. The analogy is of course imperfect. It does not indicate the sustaining nature of God as lure.

A second parable may help to fill that gap. It comes from a famous sermon of Phillips Brooks on 'The Light of the World'.[15] The world belongs to the light of the sun in the sense that its essential richness and possibility are dependent upon the sun's light. The light of the sun makes real the earth's possibilities. In the darkness of night the world is without colour, it lies torpid and wrapped up in sluggishness. When the sun rose this morning on the darkness of

the world, the fields began to grow again, its great kaleidoscope of colour became real once more, the birds began to
sing, the black streams began to sparkle, sleeping men began to think and talk and work. The sun flashed electric
invitation to the whole mass of sleeping power and sum-
moned it to action. The sun is not colour, nor the fields of
corn, nor the birds nor men. But it has intensified and fulfilled the lives of the plants and the birds and men. Light is
not life, but it sustains life.

> With part of the earth illuminated and the rest lying in the
> darkness still, we can most easily conceive of the dark region
> looking in its half-life drowsily over to the region which was
> flooded with light, and saying, There, there is the true earth!
> That is the real planet. In light and not in darkness the earth
> truly is itself.

Metaphors bewilder when we try to follow them further
than they can lead, so let us leave them and return to the
central idea of God's activity as persuader and sustainer
through his qualitative lure of the world to the fulfilment
of what is possible for it. It is in strict contrast to the idea
of complete mechanical determination of all events.

If the detail of the happenings in the universe were all
determined in exactness, then there could be no creation.
God sustains and lures, but there is spontaneity of created
nature to respond or not to respond. That is the element of
freedom of the creation. To be consistent, we must provide
for freedom at the most elementary level of matter. Without
that the idea of creation disappears. *God's creativity involves the spontaneity and freedom of the creature.* This is
an idea which is at the base of the Christian concept of the
nature of man. But is this not also a way of looking at the
whole creation? The purposes of God in creation are not
implemented as a series of arbitrary acts, but as a struggle
between a disordered state and God's lure to completeness.

In this view, cosmic evolution involves a fighting frontier
of progressive integration. 'More than two thousand years

ago the wisest of men proclaimed that the divine persuading is the foundation of the order of the world, but that it could only produce such a measure of harmony as amid brute forces it was possible to accomplish.'[18] This, Whitehead suggests, is an anticipation by Plato of a doctrine of grace, seven hundred years before its elaboration by Augustine in his fight with Pelagius. The doctrine of the divine agency as a persuasive and not a coercive agency is one of the greatest intellectual discoveries in the history of religion. Whitehead further contends that the next greatest phase of religious insight was the appeal to the life of Christ 'as a revelation of the nature of God and of his agency in the world . . . the Mother, the Child, the bare manger: the lowly man, home-less and self-forgetful, with his message of peace, love and sympathy: the suffering, the agony, the tender words as life ebbed, the final despair: the whole with the authority of supreme victory. . . . Can there be any doubt that the power of Christianity lies in its revelation in an act of that which Plato divined in theory?'[8]

The idea of the cosmos as a fighting frontier of persuasive love in a universe that contains an anarchic element has been expressed in the writings of Wieman.[16, 17, 18] He speaks of the struggle involved in the transition from one level of organization to the next. The struggle at one time may have been at the level of integration of electrons and protons. That frontier is now passed. The association of electrons and protons has achieved a stability it once did not have. There was a time when the association of atoms into living molecules was the fighting frontier. Stability is now achieved at that level. But this more subtle association is not so firmly established as that of electrons and protons in atoms. There are miscreations and misfits at the level of the cell. Cells are organized into complex organisms. Here too was a frontier at some time past. Again the creation is more delicately balanced. It is not as rigid and as apparently fixed as the atoms. When we come to man and human society, that is where integration is least achieved. Here is where chaos and disintegration are widespread and perilous. Is this then the present fighting frontier of the progressive creativity of the universe as Wieman suggests? Here is the great upreach of the human spirit to values as yet unrealized. Here the existing creation is groping into the vast realm of possibility where the undreamed values of God have their being. The challenge to man is not now mainly from his *material* environment; the challenge to struggle comes from his *spiritual* environment, the eternal realm of values. To fail to respond is not just a deficiency. It is a cosmic crisis. This is where the cosmic venture is now under way. Religion of the noblest kind is man's recognition of this cosmic struggle and his personal allegiance to the process. The one thing God cannot relieve us of is our responsibility. We find this concept expressed by Whitehead when he speaks of religion as world loyalty.[7] It is man's loyalty to the quality of the eternal environment of which his evolution has made him conscious. The picture of cosmic evolution as a struggle in which the potentially possible becomes real in the universe has in these last few years been emphasized by Tillich and Teilhard de Chardin. De Chardin traces the struggle through four stages which he calls matter, life, thought, society. Yet it is 'a single process without interruption'.

At each stage of creation God confronts what is actual in the world with what is possible for it. At the level of organization in human life, we see more clearly than elsewhere the meaning of purpose, challenge, creative struggle, freedom and spontaneity of response. Can we see imaginatively the whole of creation in this light?

Where there is freedom, there is the possibility of creation. There is also the possibility of tragedy. The freedom of man to respond to the lure of God is also the freedom not to respond. Freedom is man's opportunity and his tragedy. But the possibilities of value achieved must outweigh the risks of tragedy. There is a tragic element in human life and tragedy in nature. Again the principle of freedom at all levels of creation implies the possibility of chaos instead of order. This is a cost of creation. For God to control the world completely, to take away its freedom and spontaneity, would be to destroy it.

2. *Creation is the lifting of restraints on matter.*

This is the inverse way of looking at the realization of possibilities. There are restraints on the electron in a lone hydrogen atom compared with the electron in a hydrogen atom in a molecule of water. At another level of organization, we know that there are restraints on the properties exhibited by proteins in solution in a test-tube compared with proteins inside cells of living organisms. Presumably there are restraints on proteins in the amoeba compared with proteins in the cells of our brains. What is expressed depends upon the environment. As this evolves, the expression becomes richer. At the level of the 'living molecule' DNA (see Chapter 2), further restraints are lifted and qualities of life appear. This molecule provides the structural basis for an infinite variety of living organisms. There were restraints on life until life became organized into living man. Then the creature became self-aware and consciously pursued objectives. It had a content to life that is rich in moral and aesthetic and spiritual values. The creature became aware of what he could be in relation to what he is. He feels estranged because now he knows he is incomplete, and he becomes conscious of the struggle to become what he could be. The struggle to release the restraints on his life becomes a central consciousness of his life.

With the existence of man there is the possibility of the Christ. All restraints are lifted and the fulness of human possibility becomes concretely real in the world. In him 'there shines more of the unexplored and mysterious goodness of this universe'.[17] He is the mirror who discloses the character of God. And so Whitehead says, 'The glory of the life of Christ is for those who can discern it, and not for the world. Its power lies in the absence of force. It has the decisiveness of a supreme ideal, and that is why the history of the world divides at this point.'[19]

There was only one Christian, said Nietzsche in *Antichrist*, and he died on the cross. 'There is no just man, not one. . . . All have swerved aside . . .' said Paul (Rom. 3.11-12). What more searching interpretation of this text have we than in Origen's third-century commentary?

> How can it seem possible that no one at all can be found, whether among Jews or Gentiles . . . who has sometime given hospitality to a stranger, or bread to the hungry? . . . I cannot think that the Apostle Paul intends to make such an incredible assertion. . . . I think that he means something like this. If a man lays the foundations of a house and builds two or three walls, and collects a certain amount of material, he surely could not be said to have 'made' a house; although he has engaged in building operations. A man is said to have 'made' a house when he has brought every component part of the building to completion. This is what I think the Apostle is saying here, that no one has 'done good', that is no one has brought goodness to complete fulfilment. If we ask who is truly good and who has brought goodness to perfection we shall find only the one who says 'I am the good shepherd'.[20]

People ask, 'Why does not God make concretely real what is possible for the universe all at once? Why does he wait for billions of years for the full actualization of himself in the universe?' 'Why not proceed as in Genesis, to create man at once?' asked Bertrand Russell. 'What was the point of ichthyosaurs, dinosaurs, etc. . . ?'[21] I suggest that God does not proceed as Russell would like him to, because he is a God of creation, and not a magician. At each stage of the creative process, there are limitations on what can be actualized in the immediate future. The opportunities are limited by what has already been achieved. The existence of man was not a possible immediate step following the origin of the first 'living molecule'. One stage builds on the previous one to create a continuum. The rivers of creativity do not cut arrows direct to the sea, but wind their way by a long and sure route. As well might we ask why a child does not come into the world as a physically and emotionally mature man! That would be to deny the very nature of creation which is spontaneity of response, purpose, struggle and achievement.

Man's recognition of his own incompleteness and the consequent moral struggle is the basis of the theological doctrine called 'the fall'. The phrase 'Adam before the fall' is a highly symbolic way of expressing the potentiality of man and his recognition of his present incompleteness. The restraints that were lifted in man open up enormous possibilities and also the knowledge of the enormous gap between what a man is and what he could be. 'The actual state (of man)', says Tillich, 'is that existence in which man finds himself along with the whole universe, and there is no time in which this was otherwise. The notion of a moment in time in which man and nature were changed from good to evil is absurd, and it has no foundation in experience or revelation.'[22] The 'fall' of man and nature is a symbol of man's predicament and of the incompleteness of the natural order which is the 'evil' in nature. It is a recognition of the consequences of spontaneity and freedom in nature as well as in man.

Freedom means that God does not control the world in the sense of completely determining it. Freedom involves the possibilities of imperfection and disorder. So it is logical to say as Tillich does that 'creation and fall coincide',[22] and to reject the literal interpretation of the paradise story with its utopia in the past. Actualized creation and 'estranged creation' are identical. To ask for anything else is to ask for an irresistible might in complete control of all details. This might be a man's idea of what a power-God could do. But it is not what a God of love does. And it does not happen. The novel in each creative step is built on to the past and is not detached from it. Nothing is actualized in bare isolation. All is tied to the past and linked with the future. Creativity never ceases. No sooner has one stage been reached than another is reached for. This is the notion of perfection as dynamic and not static, of ever moving to further perfection.

For these reasons it is absurd to suppose, as some do, that Christ could have appeared in the world at any stage of its cosmic history. No, he appeared in the fullness of time. It would be still absurd to suppose that the Christ could appear in the world of no culture, the world of barbarians, if that is what our forebears were. Millennia of human history had to pass before the possibility of the manifestation of the fullness of man could become real. There is nothing modern about this view. It was clearly expressed by Origen in his *Contra Celsum* some 1,700 years ago. The potentiality of the Christ existed before Christ walked this earth. In a symbolic sense, and it is only symbolic, it is true to say that the Christ 'existed from the foundation of the world', not in concrete existence but in potential existence. All things existed in their potential in God's primordial nature. The original elemental building blocks, the electrons and the rest of the electron-like particles, were of such a nature as to be able to support the concrete realization of God in the rest of the world's evolution. They were the acorns that could sustain the development of the oaks. The acorn is not the oak, but it can sustain the development of the oak. Tillich expresses the same idea when he says: 'Symbolically speaking, one could say that when God created the potentiality of the atom within himself he created the potentiality of man.'[10] The physical world is 'germane' to God, and can therefore be the arena of his activity. He does not need to intervene as a stranger. He is no stranger. He is already there.

We have no need in this view for sharp boundaries between inorganic and organic, non-living and living, mental and physical. What emerge in higher levels of organization such as man, may exist in embryonic form in principle all the way down the scale to the electron type. We cannot see any boundaries. What we see is the results of the transitions.

It was a mistake of theology ever to suppose that God's role is to intervene into an otherwise Godless world, to provide something supernatural enabling nature to jump from non-living to living and from pre-man to man. Tillich makes the point well when he writes:

> Some theologians argued for the existence of God on the basis of our ignorance of the genesis of organic out of inorganic; they asserted that the 'first cell' can be explained only in terms of special divine interference. Obviously, biology had to reject the establishment of such a supra-natural causality and to attempt to narrow our ignorance about the conditions for the appearance of organisms—an attempt which has been largely successful.[10]

Tillich goes on to point out that these considerations involve the rejection of the doctrine that at a precise moment of the evolutionary process, God, in a special act, added an 'immortal soul to an otherwise complete human body, with the soul becoming the life of the spirit'. We think of God as revealing himself in special acts at distant intervals. But if God is love, then he reveals himself at all times in all ways and not just in special acts. If all existence is grounded in God, then all existence is a medium of revelation of the nature of God. If man is a vehicle of revelation then all men are, and so is all history and not just the history of one group of people at one particular time. This view was very strongly stated by Temple.[23] We need to recapture it today if we are to find any meaning to God's activity in the modern world.

3. *In creation the 'creature' becomes more 'aware' with each creative advance.*

Awareness is a familiar concept when used in relation to man. It obviously has meaning in relation to other animals like cats and dogs. We may be less willing to apply the term to the amoeba perhaps, though if an amoeba were the size of our dog, we might feel differently about that. Since the amoeba does respond to stimuli, is there any reason to deny it an awareness of the stimulus? I have gone further and proposed that all organized entities in the universe, be they electrons or atoms or amoeba or men, are sentient and experiencing creations. I have referred to Whitehead's use of the word 'feeling' for the electron. Whatever he may mean, he clearly does not mean that 'feeling' at that level has the exact meaning it has at the human level. It has an analogous meaning. It is the mental aspect of the entity electron. In this sense all the universe feels God. What the electron 'feels' in an atom of sodium chloride is different from the experience of a man who consciously is aware of God. We do not know what may be the nature of the inner being of the electron. We begin to have some imaginative ideas when we come to that level of organization we call living cells. An amoeba is sensitive to touch but little else perhaps. Some single cells are sensitive to light. Higher up the scale, a bee is sensitive to four colours, many scents and shapes. But a man can perceive some 160 grades of colour, a rich array of qualities of beauty, of goodness and all that may be called spiritual qualities.

There is a richness of feeling and awareness which can be the life of a man which is not possible for the cow or any other creature. Since the qualitative realm that is 'felt' is included in what in Whitehead's terms is the primordial nature of God, then it is true to say that all entities reflect the nature (or image) of God. The significance of man is that aspect of God of which he is consciously aware, namely the realm of spiritual qualities of courage, hope, forgiveness and all other elements of love. Since these are personal qualities, it is true to say that God is personal.

The evolutionary hierarchy of levels of increasing sensitivity to the qualitative environment which is God is illustrated by an analogy which Hartshorne[24] uses in another context. We might imagine someone to read aloud a poem in the presence of a glass of water, an ant, a dog, a man unacquainted with the language of the poem, a man knowing the language but insensitive to poetry, a person sensitive to poetry and knowing the language. Each member of the series is superior to its predecessors in terms of its sensitivity to the poem. The molecules of the water at one end are, at most, affected by the sound waves only slightly. The ant will hear something. The dog may be influenced by tone of voice, the human being not knowing the language may appreciate the rhythm, the insensitive but comprehending listener may get a variety of images, though without any intensity of feeling. The adequate listener may go through a deep adventure of thought and feeling. His experience will have a depth the others lack.

Oman[25] has compared the evolution of life to the evolution of a dwelling-place which grows in hospitality as it becomes more complete. First it is a cellar dark and confined; little is admitted to its barricaded entrance. But as life builds higher it opens all the windows and gateways of the senses and becomes hospitable to friendly meaning. It looks out upon an ever widening horizon of the world around it.

> *Build thee more stately mansions, O my soul,*
> *As the swift seasons roll!*
> *Leave thy low-vaulted past!*
> *Let each new temple, nobler than the last,*
> *Shut thee from heaven with a dome more vast,*
> *Till thou at length art free,*
> *Leaving thine outgrown shell by life's unresting*
> *sea![26]*

To live insensitive to the wealth of experience that can be man's is to live unfulfilled lives. We all do. We walk by on the other side when the Christ stops in his path wherever there is human need for care. One day it is the sight of a funeral procession crossing the desert, followed by the distraught widow whose only son is dead. But Jesus is no passer-by, he moves in with infinite passion and concern. His heart floods out toward the grief-stricken woman. So too when all an adulterous woman had to her comfort were her accusers, Jesus becomes the hope of a new life. The lonely Zacchaeus longs for friendship. In all the passing crowd, only Jesus knows, and so that night Zacchaeus discovered a friendship that changed his world. No man ever lived closer to life. No man ever felt the agony and the joy of life as he felt them. Tenderness and compassion flood down from the cross. Even in death the body, broken by the insensibilities of men, has ever been portrayed in the Pietas as utmost compassion.

4. *Creation is the reaction of the world upon God as well as the action of God upon the world.*

This is Whitehead's famous proposition: 'It is as true to say that God creates the World, as that the World creates God.'[3] The second part of this proposition refers to that aspect of the being of God which is the enrichment of his experience as the possible becomes concretely real in the world. If one asks what possible evidence there could be for that, the answer must be, 'None whatsoever, if by evidence you mean that which can either prove or disprove the hypothesis.' It is in the nature of a judgment of value which grows out of the propositions already entertained which in themselves make sense of the world as we understand it. The logical positivist will reject any such speculations as insubstantial. The metaphysician searches for meanings which reach beyond the certainties of simple proofs.

If there are grounds for the proposition that God is

love that gives, then it is reasonable to propose that God is love that receives. He is not passive and unmoved, when that which is potential in his primordial nature becomes actual in the world. If this is not the case, then it is difficult to defend the use of the word love in relation to God. Love is reciprocal. It is to give and to receive. Both lover and loved are moved.

Whitehead speaks of two aspects to God's nature, his 'primordial nature' and his 'consequent nature'.[3] The consequent nature of God is the nature of God consequent upon his actualization in the world. In his consequent nature God becomes 'conscious'. He experiences the world in all its immediacy and in all its detail. His consequent nature endlessly acquires richer and newer content with the world's creative advance. In his primordial nature, God proffers values. In his consequent nature, he conserves values. In his consequent nature, God is the 'unification of all things'.[3] Hartshorne has said that 'things always add up to something; for God never fails to perform the addition'.[27] Williams says, 'In God the world's action receives its final unity, its immediacy is retained, and it is transformed by his wisdom'.[12] The unity of all things is God's feeling of all feelings. It is not objects that he feels but the feeling content of entities. His is the 'feeling of feeling'.

All that is of value, that has become real in the world, is saved in God's consequent nature. This is the way God 'saves the creation' whereby it achieves immortality. 'The image—and it is but an image—', says Whitehead, 'the image under which this operative growth of God's nature is best conceived, is that of a tender care that nothing be lost.'[13] The world will one day cease to be. This order will collapse as it either freezes up or melts. Is then all that has been achieved for naught? In the doctrine of the consequent nature of God the values of creation are saved in God's experience. He is not only the beginning but also the end, both the *alpha* and the *omega*. The ocean of God's experience is the experience of all created value, including that in man. The merest puff of existence is not without its significance to God, said Whitehead on one occasion. There is no such thing as 'mere' matter. There is importance to God in the passing moment of existence. Our response to creation is restricted. God's response is boundless.

Most of traditional Christianity gives us the picture of a God who impassively observes the scene of creation, but is unmoved by it. Was there then no movement in God's nature when man first appeared on the scene? And what of God when, for the first time, the possibilities of human life were fulfilled and Christ became the first real man, man as God means him to be? Or is it nearer to the nature of love to think of this event as the flowering of the universe which enriches the universe and the God of the universe? Stephen Neill suggests,

> What God had so long looked for at last He saw—in a human mind that was able to grasp His purpose, in a human heart that manifested perfectly the divine quality of love, in a human will perfectly surrendered to His will even unto death. And what Jesus achieved, He achieved not for Himself only, but, because of that real unity of the human race in which we are all bound together, for us all.[28]

The plant that flowers is radically different after the flowering. This is a tremendous experience in the life of the plant. When the universe flowered in Christ, it was no longer exactly the same universe as it was before. It was for ever richer, and so is God. This is a radically different view from the idea that God 'condescended' to become man. Incarnation is not condescension, but the very life of God.[29]

This is a neglected aspect of theology. The main line of Christian theology has held to what is called the 'impassibility' of God, i.e. the belief that God cannot suffer or otherwise change. But the idea of God as responsive to joy and suffering is a theme which can be found in Hebrew thought, all the way from Genesis to Paul. It is implicit in the sayings of Jesus. 'Are not sparrows two a penny? Yet without your Father's leave not one of them can fall to the ground. As for you, even the hairs of your head have all been counted' (Matt. 10.29-30). Taken literally, these sayings of Jesus are non-sense. As symbols, they capture a meaning in the creation that we have lost. The sparrow may have no value in human eyes. It is worth nothing at all—but not to God. Paul speaks of God, not as the outsider afar off, but as himself involved in all that is and in the struggle of man. In Raven's para-phrase of Romans 8.26, 'God's spirit comes in alongside us, sharing in our agony, groaning with groanings unspeakable as he succours and sustains. . . .'[30] In the third century Origen wrote this: 'The Father himself and the God of the whole universe is longsuffering, full of mercy and pity. Must he not then, in some sense, be exposed to suffering? The Father himself is not impassible. . . . He feels, in some sort, the passion of love . . . and for us men he endures the passions of mankind.'[31] So in our own day, Whitehead writes, 'God is the great companion—the fellow sufferer who understands'.[3]

This is not a picture of a God 'out there', but of God living in the creation. The picture is not to be labelled 'pantheism', which is the identification of God with the universe. It is important to make the distinction between pantheism and this view which Hartshorne has called 'pan-entheism'.[24] Those who see nature as inherently low grade and evil like to brand any view of God's activity in nature as pantheism. It is a bad word as 'communism' is in some circles. But we are saying that God is both immanent in the world in his actualization in the world and transcendent to the world in that a part of his primordial nature as yet un-actualized; transcendent too in his consequent nature.

5. Creation is the unity of nature in God.

The doctrine of God's creative activity involves the unity in God of the multiplicity of entities in the world. All entities are, in this view, sustained by God and become part of God's experience. The inner life of the world is the life of God's experience. What we see as many, God presumably knows as one. Creation is all of a piece. Francis Thompson wrote:

> *All things by immortal power*
> *Near and far*
> *Hiddenly*
> *To each other linkèd are,*
> *That thou canst not stir a flower*
> *Without troubling of a star.*[32]

The poet may have in mind the universal principle of gravitation wherein the movement of the tiniest flower has some effect, immeasurably small though it be, on a star a billion light years away. There is that sort of physical unity of the universe. Every entity 'feels' every other entity 'physically'. But he may be speaking also of the mental unity of the universe, wherein the mental pole of all entities 'feels' the qualities that characterize them and that constitute the primordial nature of God.

If every part of nature participates in the divine activity, there is a sense in which to know a part would be to know the whole. But our knowledge even of the minutest part is incomplete and an abstraction. So Tennyson wrote:

> *Flower in the crannied wall,*
> *I pluck you out of the crannies—*
> *Hold you here, root and all, in my hand,*
> *Little flower—but if I could understand*
> *What you are, root and all, and all in all,*
> *I should know what God and man is.*

The little flower participates in the universal activity of God. If we could know that participation, we would know what God is. To know its participation we would have to be the flower or to be God. Its experience is denied us. The same thought is suggested by a saying of the early Egyptian

Christians which they attributed to Christ, 'Cleave the wood and I am there'.

William Blake sees 'a world' in a grain of sand and in the little winged fly:

> Seest thou the little wingèd fly, smaller than a grain of sand?
> It has a heart like thee, a brain open to heaven and hell,
> Withinside wondrous and expansive: its gates are not clos'd;
> I hope thine are not. Hence it clothes itself in such array:
> Hence thou art cloth'd with human beauty; thou mortal man.
> Seek not thy heavenly father then beyond the skies.[33]

The 'within' of the little flower in crannied wall or of the little winged fly, I only dimly see and cannot feel. But the God within human life I can know, and I may reasonably believe that he is the ground of all there is. I can never see the oneness of the universe in abstraction from personality, in abstraction from man, in abstraction from the fulness of man which is Christ. If any meaning at all can be found in the universe in abstraction from personal life, it will be a false meaning. The vision of what man is in relation to God is the source of the doctrine of creation, of God's activity in all things. When we see man in relation to the ground of his being, God, we see all things thereafter differently.

> Earth's crammed with heaven,
> And every common bush afire with God;
> But only he who sees, takes off his shoes.[34]

We may catch something of this meaning in the story Tillich tells in a sermon entitled 'Nature, also, mourns for a lost good'.[35] A Chinese emperor commissioned a famous painter to paint a picture of a rooster for him. The first year went by and no picture appeared. The painter said he had only just begun to perceive the surface of the nature of the rooster. Yet another year passed, the painter confessed at the end of it that he had only then begun to penetrate into the essence of that kind of life. After ten years of concentration on the nature of the rooster, the picture was completed, 'a work described as an inexhaustible revelation of the divine ground of the universe as expressed in one small part of it, a rooster'.

6. *God who is creator is also redeemer.*

Our thoughts about God have travelled from the God who redeems estranged human life to God as the ground of all that is. The God who redeems seems 'nearer than hands and feet, closer than breathing'. But God as creator of the universe tends to cast our minds into outer space to the remote and impersonal. We tend to think of these aspects of God in two categories, even two gods as did the Gnostics. There stands to public view today, as in the day of Jesus, the persuasiveness of the eternal ideals alongside the apparent compulsive brute force of so much of the universe. Can we reconcile these apparent incompatibilities? The notion of God as supreme mechanical power and absolute despot has stood in the way, and has led to doctrines of creation, grace and atonement which are both crude and repulsive. But another way opens up when we take persuasive love seriously as the one principle of all creation, working within a creation that has as well its own freedom for self-determination. The principle of divine love is symbolized by the cross. Love was not suspended then, though the bearer of that love was subjected to the brute forces of the world.

The destructive forces of nature are to Schweitzer an enigma in a world where he finds love as the highest principle. He speaks of God within as love with which he is united. But nature's forces are enigmatical, at one time creative and at another destructive, sometimes serving an end and sometimes not. In the world, God seems to be an impersonal force. In human life he is 'supreme ethical will'.

There is an ocean—cold water with motion. In this ocean, however, is the Gulf Stream, hot water flowing from the

equator towards the pole. . . . Similarly in God, there is the
God of love within the God of the forces of the universe—
one with Him and yet so totally different. We let ourselves
be seized and carried away by the vital stream.[36]

There is difficulty in holding together creative redemption
in man and creativity in the rest of the universe. But is not
part of our difficulty our tendency to think of creativity in
terms of power and our failure to understand the nature of
love?

The biblical theme is that Creator and Redeemer are one.
Second Isaiah leads from the one to the other:

> Who hath measured the waters in the hollow of his hand,
> and meted out heaven with the span, and comprehended the
> dust of the earth in a measure, and weighed the mountains
> in scales, and the hills in a balance? (Isa. 40.12).
>
> He giveth power to the faint; and to him that hath no
> might he increaseth strength. . . . They that wait upon the
> Lord shall renew their strength; they shall mount up with
> wings as eagles; they shall run, and not be weary; they shall
> walk, and not faint (Isa. 40.29-31).

Accordingly St John opens his Gospel thus, in the New
English Bible translation:

> . . . Through him all things came to be; no single thing
> was created without him. All that came to be was alive with
> his life, and that life was the light of men.

Hartshorne has said that the religious idea in its best
ethical form 'is that of a cosmic setting of men, and of all
things, the consciousness of which exhibits them as more
beautiful, more lovable than they appear when we ignore
this setting'.[29] The peculiar character of religion, said
Whitehead, is that it brings into consciousness that perma-
nent side of the universe that we can care for.

And yet there does remain an ultimate mystery when all
that can be said is said. There remains a great incomplete-

ness in our understanding as we try to grasp in the one vision the God who knows the electrons in outermost space and the God who feels our innermost suffering. We come to a point where clarity is no longer possible. Let us face it, 'we do not know exactly and distinctly even a single concrete item of the universe', says Hartshorne.[24] What we call 'knowledge' of any concrete entity is 'mostly ignorance and for the rest mostly guesswork and probability. In the highest sense of "knowledge", namely, direct, infallible, concrete, clearly conscious apprehension, we human subjects can scarcely be said to have any knowledge.'[13]

Is there any assurance? Can I ever have a sense of a firm foundation? What certainty I have seems to me to have faith as its starting point. By faith I mean the conviction that comes from being grasped by the importance of some things over others. They grasp us, not we them. The philosopher starts where he will. The religious person starts where he must. His spirit surrenders to the claim of spirit. What I now experience of God, I shall spend the rest of my life in searching out by reason. My awareness provides me with the presupposition of all that I reason about. In my search, reason is indispensable. But even so reason does not have the last word. It is subservient even in the moment of its triumph.

John Smith, speaking to students in seventeenth-century Cambridge, said: 'We must see with our eyes, and hear with our ears, and our hands must handle the words of life . . . David, when he would teach us how to know what the divine Goodness is, calls not for speculation but sensation: *Taste and see how good the Lord is*.'[37]

Or as Job said: 'I uttered that which I understood not, things too wonderful for me, which I knew not . . . I had heard of thee by the hearing of the ear; but now mine eye seeth thee' (42.3-5).

REFERENCES

These references are intended mainly as a guide to further reading. Bibliographical details are given at the first reference only.

PREFACE

1. J. Wren-Lewis, *Religion in the Scientific Age*. 11th Vaughan Memorial Lecture. Gazelle Press, Doncaster, 1963.
2. John E. Smith, *Reason and God*. Yale University Press, 1961.
3. *Science before Darwin*. An Anthology of British Scientific writing in the Early Nineteenth Century, ed. B. I. Cohen and H. M. Jones, André Deutsch, London, 1963.

1 · THE UNIVERSE

1. C. Hartshorne, 'Whitehead's Novel Intuition', in *Alfred North Whitehead: Essays on his Philosophy*, ed. G. L. Kline. Prentice Hall, New Jersey, 1963.
2. B. Willey, *The Eighteenth Century Background*. Chatto and Windus, London, 1940.
3. M. B. Hesse, *Science and the Human Imagination*. SCM Press, London, 1954.
4. A. N. Whitehead, *Science and the Modern World*. Cambridge University Press, 1926.
5. B. Willey, *The Seventeenth Century Background*. Chatto and Windus, London, 1934.
6. H. Butterfield, *The Origins of Modern Science*. Bell and Sons, London, 1950.
7. R. G. Collingwood, *The Idea of Nature*. Clarendon Press, Oxford, 1945.
8. J. Needham, 'Mechanistic Biology and the Religious Consciousness', in *Science, Religion and Reality*, ed. J. Needham. Sheldon Press, London, 1925.
9. C. E. Raven, *Natural Religion and Christian Theology*. First Series: *Science and Religion*. Cambridge University Press, 1953.

10. J. Ray, *The Wisdom of God Manifested in the Works of the Creation*. J. F. Dove, London, 1827.
11. C. Singer, 'Historical Relations of Religion and Science', in *Science, Religion and Reality*, ed. J. Needham.
12. C. E. Raven, *John Ray, Naturalist*. Cambridge University Press, (2nd ed.) 1950.
13. English trans. by F. J. Brand, in *Amoenitales*, vol. II. 1787.
14. J. Dillenberger, *Protestant Thought and Natural Science*. Collins, London, 1961.
15. F. Darwin, *Life and Letters of Charles Darwin*, vol. II. Murray, London, 1961.
16. F. J. Powicke, *The Cambridge Platonists*. Dent, London, 1926.
17. D. Basson, *David Hume*. Penguin Books, London, 1958.
18. *The Tables Turned*.
19. *In Memoriam*.
20. *To the Deists in Jerusalem*.
21. In (2nd) Nonesuch Edition, p. 148.
22. J. Bronowski, *A Man without a Mask (William Blake 1757-1827)*. Secker and Warburg, London, 1944.
23. B. Willey, *More Nineteenth Century Studies*. Chatto and Windus, London, 1956.
24. Reprinted in T. H. Huxley, *Lay Sermons, Essays and Reviews*. Macmillian, London, 1870.
25. Quoted by W. L. Sumner, 'Moral Education: Science and Society', in *Nature*, 201, 961-62 (1964).
26. David Lack, *Evolutionary Theory and Christian Belief*. Methuen, London, 1957.
27. C. E. Raven, *St Paul and the Gospel of Jesus*. SCM Press, London, 1961.
28. L. Huxley, *Life and Letters of Thomas Henry Huxley*. Appleton, New York, 1901.

2 · DARWIN'S CENTURY

1. E. Gosse, *Father and Son*. Penguin Books, London, 1949.
2. E. L. Mascall, *Christian Theology and Natural Science*. Longmans Green, London, 1956.
3. T. Dobzhansky *Mankind Evolving*. Yale University Press, New Haven, 1962.
4. E. Brunner, *The Christian Doctrine of Creation and Redemption*. Lutterworth Press, London, and Westminster Press, Philadelphia, 1952.
5. T. Dobzhansky, *Evolution, Genetics and Man*. Wiley, New York, 1955.

6. R. A. Fisher, *The Genetical Theory of Natural Selection*. Clarendon Press, Oxford, 1930.

7. Sewall Wright, 'The Genetical Theory of Natural Selection', *Journal of Heredity* 21, 349-56 (1930).

8. J. C. Greene, *The Death of Adam*. Mentor Books, New York, 1961.

9. W. Macneile Dixon, *The Human Situation*. Edward Arnold, London, 1937.

10. T. Dobzhansky, 'Evolution as a Creative Process', *Proc. 9th Int. Cong. Genetics*. (*Caryologia* Suppl., 1954, pp. 435-48.)

11. R. A. Fisher, 'Retrospect of the Criticisms of the Theory of Natural Selection', in *Evolution as a Process*, ed. J. Huxley, A. C. Hardy and E. B. Ford. Allen and Unwin, London, 1954.

12. C. H. Waddington, 'Evolution: the Appearance of Design in Living Things', in *Discovery*, Methuen, London, 1961.

13. C. H. Waddington, *The Strategy of the Genes*, Allen and Unwin, London, 1957.

14. T. Dobzhansky, 'Scientific Explanation—Chance and Antichance in Organic Evolution', in *Philosophy of Science*, ed. B. Baumrin (Delaware Seminar, vol. I), pp. 209-22. Wiley, New York, 1963.

15. E. Mayr, 'Accident or Design, the Paradox of Evolution', in *The Evolution of Living Organisms*, ed. G. Leeper. Melbourne University Press, 1962.

16. T. Dobzhansky, *The Biological Basis of Human Freedom*. Columbia University Press, New York, 1956.

17. J. Huxley, *The Uniqueness of Man*. Chatto and Windus, London, 1941.

18. W. H. Thorpe, *Learning and Instinct in Animals*. Harvard University Press, Cambridge, Mass., 1956.

19. Sewall Wright, 'Gene and Organism', in *American Naturalist*, 87, 5-18 (1953).

20. Teilhard de Chardin, *The Phenomenon of Man*. Collins, London, and Harper, New York, 1959.

21. C. Hartshorne, *The Logic of Perfection*. Open Court, La Salle, Illinois, 1962.

3 · CHANCE AND PURPOSE

1. F. Darwin, *Life and Letters of Charles Darwin*, vol. II.

2. A. H. Dupree, *Asa Gray*. Harvard University Press, Cambridge, Mass., 1959.

3. J. C. Greene, *Darwin and the Modern World View*, Louisiana State University Press, 1961.

4. A. H. Dupree, *Asa Gray: Darwiniana*. Harvard University Press, Cambridge, Mass., 1963.

5. C. E. Raven, *Natural Religion and Christian Theology*. First Series: *Science and Religion*.

6. Bentley Glass, 'The Relation of the Physical Sciences to Biology—Indeterminancy and Causality', in *Philosophy of Science*, ed. B. Baumrin, pp. 223-57.

7. G. G. Simpson, *The Meaning of Evolution*. Yale University Press, New Haven, 1944.

8. R. O. Kapp, 'Living and Lifeless Machines', in *Brit. Journal Philosoph. Science*, 5, 91-103 (1954).

9. C. Hartshorne, *The Philosophy and Psychology of Sensation*. University of Chicago Press, 1934.

10. H. Dingle, 'René Descartes, 1596-1650' in *Nature*, 165, 213 (1950).

11. W. Temple, *Nature, Man and God*. Macmillan, London, 1934.

12. S. Toulmin, *The Philosophy of Science*. Harper Torchbook, New York, 1960.

13. A. N. Whitehead, *Process and Reality*. Macmillan, London, 1929.

14. *The Tables Turned*.

15. J. H. Woodger, *Biological Principles*. Routledge and Kegan Paul, London, 1929.

16. W. Heisenberg, *Physics and Philosophy*. Harper Torchbook, New York, 1962.

17. C. A. Coulson, *Science and Christian Belief*. Oxford University Press, 1955.

18. C. E. Raven, *Natural Religion and Christian Theology*. Second Series: *Experience and Interpretation*. Cambridge University Press, 1953.

19. *Reality: A New Correlation of Science and Religion*, ed. B. H. Streeter. Macmillan, London, 1929.

20. A. N. Whitehead, *The Concept of Nature*. Cambridge University Press, 1920.

21. F. A. Iremonger, *William Temple, Archbishop of Canterbury*. Oxford University Press, 1948.

22. J. Oman, *The Natural and the Supernatural*. Cambridge University Press, 1931.

23. L. C. Birch, 'Interpreting the Lower in terms of the Higher', in *The Christian Scholar*, 37, 402-407 (1954).

24. W. R. Inge, 'Origen' in *Proc. British Academy*, 32, 1-23. Oxford University Press, London, 1946.

25. H. H. Farmer, *The World and God*. Nisbet, London, 1935.

26. C. E. Raven, *Jesus and the Gospel of Love*. Hodder and Stoughton, London, 1931.

27. G. F. Woods, *Theological Explanation*. Nisbet, London, 1958.

28. F. R. Tennant, *Philosophical Theology*. Cambridge University Press, 1928.

29. P. Tillich, *Systematic Theology*, vol. III: *Life and the Spirit. History and the Kingdom of God*. University of Chicago Press, 1963, and Nisbet, London, 1964.

30. *In Memoriam*.

31. *Lines Composed above Tintern Abbey*.

32. C. Hartshorne, *The Logic of Perfection*.

33. A. Arber, *The Mind and the Eye*. Cambridge University Press, 1954.

34. W. H. Thorpe, *Biology and the Nature of Man*. Oxford University Press, 1962.

35. Teilhard de Chardin, *Le Milieu Divin*. Collins, London, and Harper, New York, 1960.

36. P. Tillich, *Systematic Theology*, vol. II: *Existence and the Christ*. University of Chicago Press and Nisbet, London, 1957.

37. W. R. Sorley, *Moral Values and the Idea of God*. Cambridge University Press, 1918.

38. N. Hartmann, *Ethics*, vol. II: *Moral Values*. Allen and Unwin, London, 1932.

39. W. E. Agar, *A Contribution to the Theory of the Living Organism*. Melbourne University Press, 1943.

40. Sewall Wright, 'Gene and Organism', in *The American Naturalist*, 87, 5-18 (1953).

41. C. F. von Weizsäcker, *The History of Nature*. University of Chicago Press, 1940.

42. J. Needham, 'A Biologist's View of Whitehead's Philosophy', in *Time the Refreshing River*. Allen and Unwin, London, 1943.

43. A. N. Whitehead, *Science and the Modern World*.

44. T. Dobzhansky, *Mankind Evolving*.

45. René Dubos, *The Torch of Life*. Pocket Books Inc., New York, 1963.

46. Rémy Chauvin, *God of the Scientists, God of the Experiment*. Helicon Press, Baltimore, 1960.

47. J. C. Eccles, *The Neurophysiological Basis of Mind*. Clarendon Press, Oxford, 1953.

48. G. R. G. Mure, *Introduction to Hegel*. Clarendon Press, Oxford, 1940.

49. A. E. Housman, *Last Poems*.

50. P. Tillich, *The New Being*. Scribners, New York, and SCM Press, London, 1955.
51. *New Essays in Philosophical Theology*, ed. A. Flew and A. MacIntyre. SCM Press, London, and Macmillan, New York, 1955.
52. C. E. Raven, *The Earth is the Lord's*. Address to the Conference of the Institute of Rural Life at Home and Overseas, London, 1954.
53. J. Oman, *Grace and Personality*. Cambridge University Press, 1917.
54. C. Hartshorne, *The Divine Relativity*. Yale University Press, New Haven, 1948.
55. C. Hartshorne, *Reality as Social Process*. Free Press, Glencoe, Illinois, 1953.
56. J. Sittler, *Called to Unity*. World Council of Churches, Third Assembly, New Delhi, 1961.
57. A. N. Whitehead, *Religion in the Making*. Cambridge University Press, 1930.
58. W. Barclay, *The Letters to Philippians, Colossians, Thessalonians*. Saint Andrew Press, Edinburgh, 1959.
59. J. Macmurray, 'Science and Religion', in *The Expository Times*, 61, 72-73 (1959).
60. P. Tillich, *The Theology of Culture*. Oxford University Press, 1953.

4 · CREATION AND THE BIBLE

1. A. Richardson, *Genesis 1-11: The Creation Stories and the Modern World View*. Torch Bible Paperbacks, SCM Press, London, 1964.
2. R. Bultmann, *Primitive Christianity*. Meridian Books, New York, 1962.
3. J. Wren-Lewis, 'Science and the Doctrine of Creation', in *The Expository Times*, 71, 80-82 (1959).
4. C. Westermann, 'God and his Creation' in *Union Seminary Quarterly Review*, 18, 197-209 (1963).
5. K. Barth, *Church Dogmatics*, III 2: *The Doctrine of Creation*. T. and T. Clark, Edinburgh, 1960.
6. P. Tillich, *Systematic Theology*, vol. I. University of Chicago Press, 1951.
7. L. Gilkey, *Maker of Heaven and Earth*. Doubleday, New York, 1959.
8. D. Evans, *The Logic of Self-Involvement*. SCM Press, London, 1963.

9. C. E. Raven, *Natural Religion and Christian Theology*. First Series: *Science and Religion*.
10. E. Leach, 'Genesis as Myth', in *Discovery*, 23, 30-35 (1962).
11. C. S. Elton, *Voles, Mice and Lemmings*. Clarendon Press, Oxford, 1942.
12. J. Pelikan, 'Creation and Causality in the History of Christian Thought', in *Evolution after Darwin*, ed. S. Tax, vol. III, University of Chicago Press, 1960.
13. A. N. Whitehead, *Religion in the Making*. Cambridge University Press, 1930.
14. E. L. Mascall, *Christian Theology and Natural Science*.
15. Ralph Hodgson, *The Bells of Heaven*.

5 · THE MEANING OF CREATION

1. Cambridge University Press, 1920.
2. Arthur Koestler, *The Sleepwalkers*. Hutchinson, London, and Macmillan, New York, 1959.
3. A. N. Whitehead, *Process and Reality*. Macmillan, London.
4. T. H. Huxley, 'On the Reception of the Origin of Species', in F. Darwin, *The Life and Letters of Charles Darwin*, vol. II.
5. P. Tillich, *Systematic Theology*, vol. I.
6. N. Berdyaev, *The Destiny of Man*. Scribners, New York, and Bles, London, 1937.
7. A. N. Whitehead, *Religion in the Making*.
8. A. N. Whitehead, *Adventures of Ideas*. Cambridge University Press, 1933.
9. C. Hartshorne, 'Whitehead and Contemporary Philosophy', in *The Relevance of Whitehead*, ed. I. Leclerc. Macmillan, New York, and Allen and Unwin, London, 1961.
10. P. Tillich, *Systematic Theology*, vol. III.
11. J. Baillie, *Natural Science and the Spiritual Life*. Oxford University Press, 1951.
12. D. D. Williams, 'Deity, Monarchy and Metaphysics', in *The Relevance of Whitehead*, ed. I. Leclerc.
13. C. Hartshorne, and W. L. Reese, *Philosophers Speak of God*. University of Chicago Press, 1953.
14. W. E. Hocking, *Science and the Idea of God*. University of North Carolina Press, 1944.
15. Phillips Brooks, *The Light of the World and other Sermons*. Macmillan, London, 1892.
16. H. N. Wieman, *Religious Experience and Scientific Method*. Macmillan, New York, 1927.

17. H. N. Wieman, *Methods of Private Religious Living*. Macmillan, New York, 1929.

18. H. N. Wieman, *The Source of Human Good*. University of Chicago Press, 1946.

19. A. N. Whitehead, *Science and the Modern World*. Cambridge University Press, 1926.

20. Quoted from *The Early Christian Fathers*, ed. H. Bettenson, Oxford University Press, 1956.

21. B. Russell, *Religion and Science*. Home University Library, Thornton Butterworth, London, 1935.

22. P. Tillich, *Systematic Theology*, vol. II.

23. W. Temple, *Nature, Man and God*.

24. C. Hartshorne, *The Divine Relativity*.

25. J. Oman, *The Natural and the Supernatural*.

26. Oliver Wendell Holmes, *The Chambered Nautilus*.

27. C. Hartshorne, 'Whitehead's Novel Intuition', in *Alfred North Whitehead: Essays on his Philosophy*, ed. G. L. Kline.

28. S. Neill, *Christian Faith Today*. Pelican Books, London, 1955.

29. C. Hartshorne, *Reality as Social Process*.

30. C. E. Raven, *Christ and the Modern Opportunity*. SCM Press, London, 1956.

31. Origen in *Homilies*, quoted from *The Early Christian Fathers*, ed. H. Bettenson.

32. *The Mistress of Vision XXII*.

33. *Heart and Brain*.

34. Elizabeth Barrett Browning, *Aurora Leigh*, Book VII.

35. P. Tillich, *The Shaking of the Foundations*. Scribners, New York, and SCM Press, London, 1953.

36. A. Schweitzer, *Christianity and the Religions of the World*. G. H. Doran and Co., New York, 1932.

37. B. Willey, *The Seventeenth Century Background*.

INDEX